ADAM SPENCER

MA+HS
101

The curly maths questions
your primary school kids will
ask you (WITH THE ANSWERS!)

Hardie Grant

BOOKS

CONTENTS

INTRODUCTION

I guess I'm lucky in some ways. Mathematics has always been the most beautiful and logical thing going on for me. Ever since primary school, I just 'got it'.

Times tables – loved them and still do. Long division – cool! I mean, how else can you figure out the volume of a rectangular prism?

But I also know maths doesn't make instant sense for everyone and no matter how much sense it might have made for you 'back in the day', the ravages of time often muddy the best of minds.

This book is for anyone who wants to truly understand primary school mathematics. It's not a cheat sheet or a series of short cuts to help you bluff your way through. This is a step-by-step guide to help you and your child deeply understand what is going on in this wonderful world.

And if that saves dad I few awkward 'um ... ask your mum, I think she knows that stuff' moments, all the better.

A few things to note:

- Try your utmost to genuinely understand something before moving to the next step. That way it sticks.
- The book doesn't contain thousands of examples – the internet and your child's textbook does. There is no substitute for practise.
- Occasionally a teacher might do something slightly differently to here. Fear not! Read my method and compare them. They are probably very similar.
- As in life, in this book the numbers appear as digits and words.
- Contact me with any questions and comments at book@adamspencer.com.au. I'd love to hear from you.

Off you go – the magic of mathematics awaits. Adam S

MATHEMATICS
before SCHOOL

I will start with a few remarks about developing a child's 'mathematical mind' in the years before they enter school. In doing so, can I make it absolutely clear that I think early childhood should be a time of fun and adventure for kids – and their parents! The last thing I would want this chapter to do is to encourage people to begin 'hothousing' their child with a heavy schedule of mathematics lessons before they even enter formal education. Nothing could be further from the truth.

At the same time, a child's natural curiosity does lead them to explore number and embryonic mathematical ideas. Give your child one biscuit and their sibling three and just sit back and watch how they have already developed a concept of the difference between one and three!!!

So the following are a few suggestions as to how you may entertain that burgeoning curiosity in a way that might also both help develop mathematical thinking and save parents from the boredom of navigating your kid through the nervous nineties so you can boast they can count to 100.

Also it's important to understand these are not activities 'strictly for kids who have not started school'. In the early years of school they will also be helpful and, hopefully, fun. Let your child progress through these sorts of things at whatever rate they feel comfortable and engaged.

Down for the count

Let me start by addressing one quite common and very understandable misconception about the young mathematical mind. It's day one at kindergarten and as they are led away from us beaming parents to begin the education journey, you proudly inform me that your son Angelo can already count to 50. With a proud grin I respond:

*'That's awesome mate. I'm happy for you. My girl, Olivia –
that's her over there – she can count to 200.'*

An understandable reaction by you, and anyone who
overhears this conversation, is to assume 'wow Adam's kid
is already soooooo much better at maths than poor Angelo;
and as they grow up, I'm sure she will pull further and
further away'. That's simply not the case.

Don't get me wrong, it's cool being able to count to 200.
But in my opinion, once you get beyond say, forty, it is really
an exercise in vocabulary as much as it is mathematics.

Here are some things you can do with your child to get
them thinking in a mathematical way beyond just learning
certain patterns in words. You'll note many of them are not
directly mathematical at all! Most of them are using things
around the house. The more you can build mathematics
into your everyday experiences, the more your child will
see its usefulness.

Problem solving

Planning an activity and getting a sense of how to organise
your thoughts in a logical fashion is great for young
mathematical minds.

Here's an example you can use before a day out:

*'What do we need to take if we want to go to the beach in our
swimmers, get dry, and then go to Nan's in the nice clothes she
brought us for Christmas?'*

*'How can we lay these things out so we know we have
everything? Can we put them down here in the order that we
will need them?'*

'Will this bag be big enough for all of your stuff?'

Piles of coins

Don't get me wrong, laying out 50 coins and asking your child to count all of them is useful in developing their mathematical skills. But the next level is to be able to associate individual words and figures with the number of items they represent. Here are a couple of things that go to that next level.

Write the numbers 1 to 20 out on pieces of cardboard.

Arrange coins in piles – they could also be buttons or old mobile phone chargers you just can't let go of!

Can your child count the number of objects and assign the correct card to them?

Can they advance and do this:

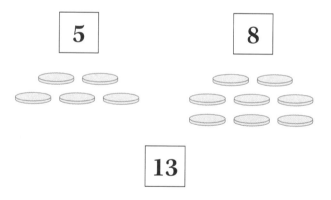

And see that 5 coins and 8 coins gives us 13 coins?

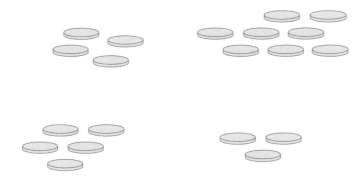

Lay out some coins as above. How many coins are in each pile? By looking at the piles can your child work out:

Which two piles could we put together to have the same number of coins as another pile?

Can they see that putting the 3 coins with the 5 coins would give a second pile of 8 coins?

Here's a harder question, looking at the coins below:

How many coins must we move from the larger pile to the smaller one to have two piles of equal size?

Your child might at first guess six. In fact it is three, because as the large pile gets smaller, the small pile also gets larger!

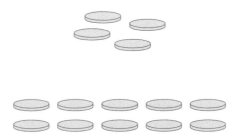

If your child can count to 30, that's a great start. But developing an understanding that each of the words in that list corresponds to a number is a deeper understanding.

Drop say 24 coins in a mass on the table and ask them to count how many are there. They may get an answer of 24, but it's quite possible they miss a coin or count some more than once.

Now get them to count ten coins by dragging them away to the side. Stack the 10 coins. Do that again. Can they see that:

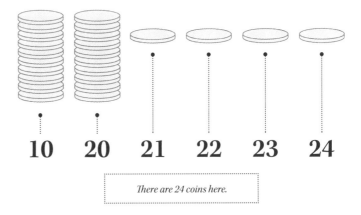

| 10 | 20 | 21 | 22 | 23 | 24 |

There are 24 coins here.

This also develops an understanding of the crucial role that 10 plays in our counting system.

Gorgeous geometry

Using a piece of cardboard make 4 triangles, all the same size, as below:

Ask your child:

Can you make them into a square?

Can you make them into two squares?

Can you make them into a bigger square with a square inside it?

Can you make them into a triangle?

What about two triangles?

Now make some other shapes and tell me what you think they look like.

Memory Match

Throughout the book I will stress that most of mathematics is best understood and not just left to memory. At the same time, good power of recall can be very helpful. Many homes have a version of 'Memory Match' on the shelves but it often gets left to gather dust after a little while. I think it rocks, so let's dust it off.

After playing for a while, ask your child, and perhaps yourself, is there a good strategy for playing?

Here are three tips:

I always found that just randomly guessing got children lost, whereas if you work along the rows methodically, you've more of a chance to remember where something was.

If you flip over a card and you have no idea where a match is, don't guess at random. You're more likely to set your opponent up with an easy pair than to fluke a pair yourself. It might be best to choose a card you know, even if you know it is not a pair for the card you just turned over.

Most players, when they think they have a pair, but they are not sure, flip the card they are certain of first and leave the guess for second. You are better to flip the card you are less sure of first. If it comes up as you hoped, finish the pair. If not and you don't know where the other card is, see the above rule and go to a safe, incorrect pick that doesn't give your opponent an easy pair.

Please understand I'm not telling you this to create an army of Olympic-level Memory Match players but showing that strategy can help when solving a problem – here matching cards – is a valuable lesson for your child.

Brilliant board games

Some famous (and not so famous) board games are great for the young mind. They encourage strategy and the ability to see ahead to positions in the game that have not yet occurred. There are many examples of this. Four of my favourites are:

Snakes and ladders – you can increase the difficulty for older children by using two or three dice.
Connect 4 – I've met 6-year-olds who play a mean game of Connect 4. It's good for developing visualisation and strategy.
Othello – the tagline used to be 'a minute to learn – a lifetime to master'. It's a great game that can easily be explained to a child.
Quarto – this lesser-known board game was invented by Swiss mathematician Blaise Muller and was voted the 2004 World Game of the Year. It rocks.

Apps

It won't surprise you to know there are hundreds of maths-related apps out there. I won't pick favourites as the field is evolving so rapidly, but I will suggest that if you choose a maths app do some research and see who has created it or who vouches for its integrity. A good app can keep your child engaged and is the perfect way, for example, to drill times tables and basic addition into a child's memory in the early years of primary school.

Online resources

If you want to look online for things to inspire a young mind, there are many places you could start. I thoroughly recommend NRICH. It's a collaboration between the faculties of Mathematics and Education at the University of Cambridge so, um yeah, they have some heft behind them. Go to **www.nrich.maths.org** and hit the 'early years' tab for some great ideas.

AMSI has lots of ideas for at home maths too on **www.calculate.org.au**

Summary

Can I please stress again, the years before school and early school are years that should be spent enjoying the wonders of the world. The last thing I want to do is encourage the hothousing of young kids who haven't even started at school yet. At the same time, in an age where children will clamour for screen time and are constantly bored, it's well worth establishing these sorts of games and activities as an enjoyable way to pass the time. Good luck and I'll see you in primary school!

WHOLE
NUMBERS

NUMBERS
and COUNTING

In our first chapter I stressed that while counting is an important skill, it is important for a child to push beyond just reciting words in an order and to actually develop a sense of numbers. Some of the activities in that chapter, which covered both before school and the early primary years, helped with this.

Another handy device your child will encounter in the early years of school that helps give a sense of the order of numbers is our old friend **the number line.**

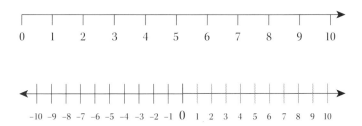

The important features of the number line are:
- 0 which is always marked on every number line.
- The arrow at the end of the line, indicating that the numbers continue in that direction ... FOREVER.
- Dashes on the line, evenly spaced apart with numbers written under them.

In the earlier years the number line will start at 0 and just show the positive numbers. After a while, negative numbers will be introduced. At this stage the number line has an arrow at each end showing that numbers go on in each direction ... FOREVER.

You can ask your child to do basic activities on the number line like 'count forward in 3s'.

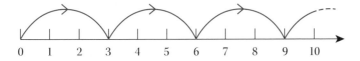

Or you can ask more complicated questions, like:

Starting at 13, count backwards by fours. What is the last positive number you will land on?

To which the answer is 1.

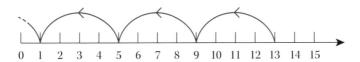

Eventually they should be just as comfortable moving on the negative side of 0.

Count backwards from 6, by 2s.

Answer: 6, 4, 2, 0, –2, –4, and so on.

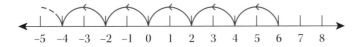

Start at negative seven and count forwards by 4s. What are the first three positive numbers you will count?

Answer: 1, 5 and 9.

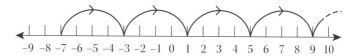

These last couple are challenging questions for a younger child. If your kid is getting this right while in grade 3 they are doing well!

Over time they should ideally be able to answer these sorts of questions without using a number line. If your child can count forward from 5 in 4s, say 5, 9, 13, 17, 21, 25, 29 ... they have a well developed sense of numbers that will really help them as mathematics becomes more advanced.

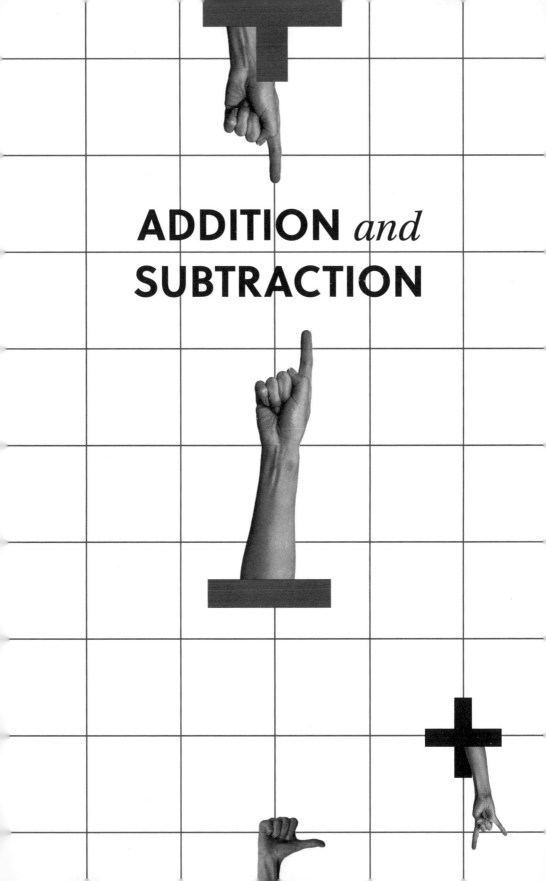

ADDITION *and* SUBTRACTION

With all of mathematics, the more practise you do the better. But nowhere is this more true for primary students than with the basic things we do to numbers: addition, subtraction, multiplication and division. We call these four things 'operations'.

I cannot stress strongly enough, it is IMPOSSIBLE for your child to do too much practice on these four operations. I know for a fact that if a child could fall ill from doing too much multiplication, I would have been in hospital for most of my primary school years!

The sensible first operation to look at is 'addition', though it is helpful to think of addition and subtraction as closely connected.

Addition

One of the great things about addition is that it can be made easier by one of its very cool properties, which we call commutativity. Don't be scared by this word. It simply means that we can swap the order of numbers around in addition and we get the same answer.

It should be obvious that if you put 3 pencils on a desk and then another 4 pencils on the same desk, you'd get exactly the same outcome as if you had put 4 pencils on the desk and followed up with 3 more. In the same way, we can see that:

$$3 + 4 = 7 \qquad 4 + 3 = 7 \qquad \text{and} \qquad 3 + 4 = 4 + 3$$

That's great for addition, but commutativity doesn't work for subtraction. Can you see that:

$$4 - 3 \neq 3 - 4$$

*This nifty little symbol represents, 'is **not** equal to'.*

Another property of addition is that it doesn't matter how we group the numbers as we add them. We call this the associative property. Again, no need to commit the A-word to memory. Just convince yourself that if we do the addition in the brackets first you can see that:

$$(3 + 4) + 5 = 7 + 5 = 12$$

and
$$3 + (4 + 5) = 3 + 9 = 12$$

so
$$(3 + 4) + 5 = 3 + (4 + 5)$$

You can check a few examples to see that associativity doesn't work for subtraction either!

Now that's all cute Adam, with your 'commutativity' and your 'associativity', but what does that have to do with my kid learning addition? Well the cool thing about these rules for addition is that if you combine the commutative property and the associative property you get the '**any order' rule for addition**.

Basically, addition of two or more numbers can be done in any order and the result is the same. This is really handy with long strings of numbers. If you try to do the following in your head you might become confused:

$$2 + 7 + 14 + 8 + 3 + 6 =$$

but rearrange the numbers into 'chunks of tens' and it is much easier:

$$14 + 6 + 8 + 2 + 3 + 7 = 20 + 10 + 10 = 40$$

But, in their younger years, your child can't do this yet. To start out we have to master how to ...

Add two numbers that are less than 10

By the end of this chapter, you and your child will know how to add together any two numbers, no matter how large. Literally adding millions to millions – bigger, if you'd like! And the really cool thing about adding together massive numbers is that you don't need to learn every possible example.

Ask me, 'Adam, what's 654 + 238' ... go on ... ask me.

I've got no idea. None. But I could work it out quickly in my head ... because that's how I roll.

I can add and subtract massive numbers in my head. But all I have committed to memory is how to add any two single digit numbers together.

FYI my thought process is this: $4 + 8 = 12$ and $5 + 3 = 8$. Now $8 + 1 = 9$ and $6 + 2 = 8$. So $654 + 238 = 892$ ... and I'll play on for the million dollars thanks Eddie.

Now don't worry yet about why I was doing the sums I did. You will learn that later. But note to add together these two big numbers, I didn't need to add together any more than some single digit numbers. I could do these all from memory after doing thousands of examples over the years.

That's the crucial thing to understand about arithmetic. The amount you commit to memory is very small. But you really have to have it deeply embedded in your mind. For your child to be comfortable with mathematics, to enjoy it and hopefully to crush the occasional exam, they really need to be completely across the basics. And in many ways there is nothing more basic than adding single digits together.

This table covers all the single digit additions from $1 + 1 = 2$ up to $9 + 9 = 18$. I've highlighted the example of $6 + 8 = 14$ on the opposite page.

+	1	2	3	4	5	6	7	8	9
1	2	3	4	5	6	7	8	9	10
2	3	4	5	6	7	8	9	10	11
3	4	5	6	7	8	9	10	11	12
4	5	6	7	8	9	10	11	12	13
5	6	7	8	9	10	11	12	13	14
6	7	8	9	10	11	12	13	14	15
7	8	9	10	11	12	13	14	15	16
8	9	10	11	12	13	14	15	16	17
9	10	11	12	13	14	15	16	17	18

You will find that adding the smaller numbers, 3 + 3 = 6, 2 + 3 = 5, 4 + 1 = 5 and so on, comes pretty easily for most children. It's when we move on to 6, 7, 8 and 9 that things get tougher. Again, the answer is lots of practice, but here's a couple of hints that may help.

Adding 9 is completely fine!

When we add 9, we can make use of the fact that 9 is very close to 10.

So when we add 6 and 9 we can take one away from the 6 and give it to the 9 ... so, by looking at the dots on the next page, we can see that 6 + 9 = 5 + 10 = 15.

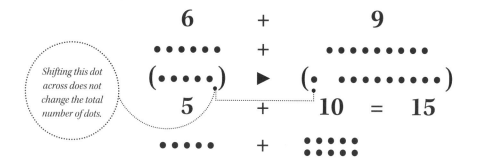

Shifting this dot across does not change the total number of dots.

$$6 + 9 = 5 + 10 = 15$$

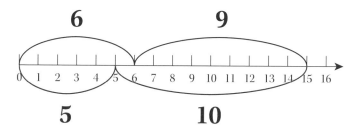

Or, by looking at the number line you can see that adding 9 is the same as adding 10 and stepping back 1.

$$6 + 9 = 6 + 10 - 1 = 16 - 1 = 15$$

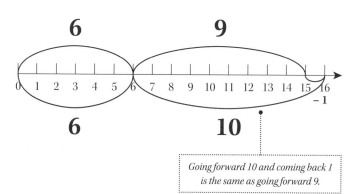

Going forward 10 and coming back 1 is the same as going forward 9.

After a while your child should be thinking ...

$$8 + 9 = 18 - 1 = 17$$

$$9 + 9 = 19 - 1 = 18$$

$$56 + 9 = 66 - 1 = 65$$

... automatically. Again, they can't practise this too much.

One way to learn the sum of the larger single digit numbers is sometimes called '**make up to a ten**'.

What is 8 + 7?

Well 8 is 2 short of 10. And 7 = 2 + 5. So you should be able to see that we can work it out this way:

$$8 + 7 = 8 + \underbrace{2 + 5}_{7} = \underbrace{8 + 2}_{10} + 5 = 15$$

Try writing out these examples taking steps like we did opposite to 'make up to a ten' and convince yourself that:

$$9 + 7 = 16; \quad 5 + 9 = 14; \quad 8 + 8 = 16$$

Again, your child will do well to do dozens and dozens of examples like this (hundreds and hundreds even!) until they become known by heart. At the end of the day there is no substitution for just doing, doing and doing again all the examples on this table. Set them challenges. Speed, accuracy, most correct in a row, give an answer like 12 and ask for three different sums that give the answer ... I don't care what you do. Just get your child adding single digits.

Adding multiple single-digit numbers

As you saw in our earlier example, sometimes you can make things simpler and 'find a ten'.

Consider $5 + 6 + 8 + 4$:

We can change the order of addition and group the 6 and the 4 because 6 + 4 = 10.

$$5 + 6 + 8 + 4 = 6 + 4 + 5 + 8$$

$$10$$

$$= 10 + 13 = 23$$

But once your child knows all of the single-digit additions, they should be able to add a string of single-digit numbers just from looking at them.

If your child knows 7 + 8 = 15, they should be able to see that 17 + 8 just jumps up to the next number that ends in a 5; 17 + 8 = 25.

Again, 5 + 9 = 14 so, with practise, 25 + 9 obviously = 34.

$$5 + 8 + 4 + 8 + 9 + 7 = 13 + 4 + 8 + 9 + 7 = 17 + 8 + 9 + 7$$

$$= 25 + 9 + 7 = 34 + 7$$

$$= 34 + 7 = 41$$

Addition algorithm

The addition algorithm is the perfect example of a common problem parents run into when discussing mathematics with their children. You know the feeling – you're pretty sure you remember what to do, you're pretty sure it gets the right result, but if your child asks 'but WHY do we do that?' things start getting a little shaky. Sound familiar?

Well one thing we will do in this book is really look under the hood and remind you not just WHAT we do in primary school maths, but WHY we do it.

I'll go through some of these things in almost painful detail. Trust me, it is best for you and your child if you do the same. Doing something until it makes sense significantly increases the likelihood it will stick for your child and they will be able to move onto more challenging concepts.

Let's start with a simple example.

What is 34 + 52? Let's do it by adding all the units together and then all the tens. Huh? Watch this:

$$34 + 52 = 4 + 30 \quad + \quad 2 + 50$$
$$= 4 + 2 \quad + \quad 30 + 50$$

$$\underbrace{\text{units}} \qquad \underbrace{\text{tens}}$$

$$= 6 \quad + \quad 80$$
$$= 86$$

Or we could have written the two numbers above each other, lining up the units and the tens, and adding them 'down the line'.

$$
\begin{array}{r}
34\ + \\
52 \\
\hline
86
\end{array}
$$

$4 + 2 = 6$

$$30 + 50 = 80$$

That was really easy. But it was easy because the units behaved themselves and didn't get too big. What happens if they do?

Let's try 34 + 58.

This time there are more than ten units in the equation and we need to make an adjustment:

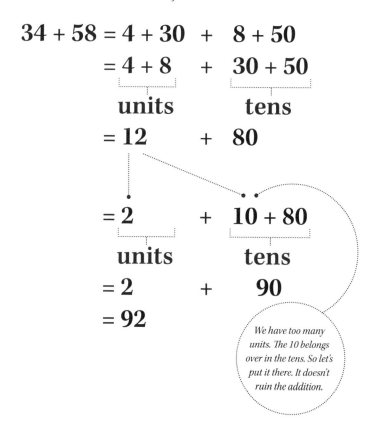

$$34 + 58 = 4 + 30 \quad + \quad 8 + 50$$
$$= 4 + 8 \quad + \quad 30 + 50$$
$$\underbrace{\text{units}} \qquad \underbrace{\text{tens}}$$
$$= 12 \quad + \quad 80$$

$$= 2 \qquad + \quad 10 + 80$$
$$\underbrace{\text{units}} \qquad \underbrace{\text{tens}}$$
$$= 2 \quad + \quad 90$$
$$= 92$$

We have too many units. The 10 belongs over in the tens. So let's put it there. It doesn't ruin the addition.

So, if we were to add the numbers 'down the line' we would have to adjust for those extra units. Here's how we do it:

$$^{1}34 + \qquad 4 + 8 = 12 = 10 + 2$$
$$58$$
$$\overline{}$$
$$... 2$$

$$^{1}34 + \qquad 10 + 30 + 50 = 90$$
$$58$$
$$\overline{}$$
$$92$$

The whole mystery of the addition algorithm and those cobwebs in the corners of your mind blow away if you can see where that 1 comes from – that 4 + 8 = 12 and that is why we write a 2 in the units column in the answer and add 1 to the tens column in the sum.

Let's do one more and let you go on your way from here.

Add 867 + 298 + 419

The long way to do this might look a bit tedious, but trust me. Do it in full and you will really 'get' the addition algorithm.

$$867 + 298 + 419 =$$

$$7 + 60 + 800 + 8 + 90 + 200 + 9 + 10 + 400$$

$$= 7 + 8 + 9 + \quad 60 + 90 + 10 \quad + \quad 800 + 200 + 400$$

units   **tens**   **hundreds**

first add the units

$$= \quad 24 \qquad 60 + 90 + 10 \quad + \quad 800 + 200 + 400$$

move the excess units
into the tens

$$= \quad 4 \quad + \quad 20 + 60 + 90 + 10 \quad + \quad 800 + 200 + 400$$

now add the tens

$$= \quad 4 \quad + \qquad 180 \qquad + \quad 800 + 200 + 400$$

move the excess tens
into the hundreds

$$= \quad 4 \quad + \qquad 80 \qquad + \quad 100 + 800 + 200 + 400$$

now add the hundreds

$$= \quad 4 \quad + \qquad 80 \qquad + \qquad 1500$$

$$= 4 + 80 + 1500$$

$$= 1584$$

And if you understand that process, you should be able to see why the addition algorithm simplifies our working to this:

$$\overset{2}{8}67 +$$
$$298$$
$$\underline{419}$$
$$\ldots 4$$

units: $7 + 8 + 9 = 24$

$$\overset{1\ 2}{8}67 +$$
$$298$$
$$\underline{419}$$
$$\text{.. } 84$$

tens: $2 + 6 + 9 + 1 = 18$

$$\overset{1\ 2}{8}67 +$$
$$298$$
$$\underline{419}$$
$$1584$$

hundreds: $1 + 8 + 2 + 4 = 15$

Go on. Convince yourself that:

$$42386 +$$
$$\underline{91570}$$
$$133956$$

In the interests of keeping this book to a manageable length, I won't give many exercises here. But that shouldn't stop you. Write down 20 examples for your child to solve and check their answers on a calculator, or find hundreds of examples in their textbooks or online and **practise, practise, practise** the addition algorithm.

Subtraction

Okay, now that we've mastered everything we could want to know about addition, let's have a crack at subtraction.

Subtraction can be thought of as the 'opposite' of addition. We maths nerds tend to say 'inverse', but 'opposite' will do.

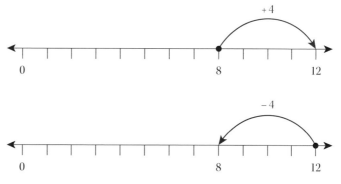

Looking at the number line it should be obvious that $8 + 4 = 12$. Hopefully you can just as easily see that $12 - 4 = 8$.

The close relationship between addition and subtraction should mean that by learning all of the single digit additions from 1 + 1 = 2 up to 9 + 9 = 18, your child also becomes proficient at simple subtraction. Knowing that 3 + 5 = 8 should lead to 8 − 5 = 3 being just as obvious. **It will take practise but it is really important to do**.

Like addition, where subtraction gets harder is when the numbers involved get bigger.

Let's consider the sum 72 − 35. Here are three ways to work it out in your head. Try each of these with your child and see which they prefer.

1. Subtract a bit at a time

To take away 35 from 72, let's take away 30, and once we've done that let's take away another 5.

(if your child understands that 12 − 5 = 7, they should see that for 42 − 5 the tens amount drops back from 40 to 30):

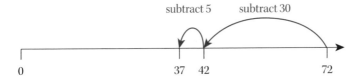

2. Start from 35 and build up to 72

In the same way that 12 − 4 = 8 meant that it was 4 units from 8 to 12, we can step from 35 to 72 this way:

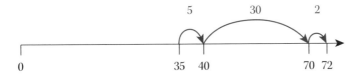

35 ... + 5 ... 40 ... + 30 ... 70 ... + 2 ... 72

So we added 5 + 30 + 2 = 37 to get from 35 to 72

So, 72 − 35 = 37

3. Add the same to both numbers to make the subtraction easier

72 – 35 must be the same as 77 – 40 because each number has increased by exactly 5. But this second subtraction is much easier because it has no units.

So, 72 – 35 = 77 – 40 = 37

Try each of these methods with lots and lots of subtractions. You can check with a calculator if you'd like (some kids get excited when the answer they get on paper or in their head matches the calc!). The more naturally simple subtraction comes for your child, the better. And yes, this is still the simple stuff!

Subtraction algorithm

Just as we found with addition, when subtraction moves to larger numbers it can get harder. But just like we found with addition, there is a handy algorithm to help us out. And just like with the addition algorithm, your child will best understand the subtraction algorithm if you proceed slowly, starting with some very simple examples.

There are two different algorithms taught in schools. Let's check them both.

1. Trading or decomposing

Let's start with a simple example. Make sure you understand the working.

What is 42 – 6?

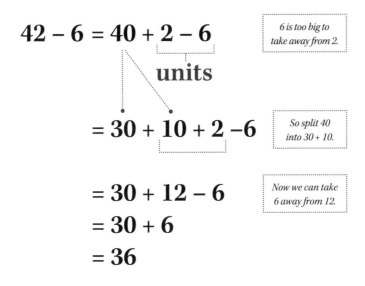

$$42 - 6 = 40 + 2 - 6$$

6 is too big to take away from 2.

units

$$= 30 + 10 + 2 - 6$$

So split 40 into 30 + 10.

$$= 30 + 12 - 6$$

Now we can take 6 away from 12.

$$= 30 + 6$$

$$= 36$$

trading

$$42 -$$
$$6$$

6 is too big to take from 2.

$$\overset{3}{\cancel{4}}\overset{1}{2} -$$
$$6$$

Split the 40 into 30 + 10, 'trade the ten for ten ones, and add it to the 2'. The 2 is now 12; the 4 in the tens column is now 3.

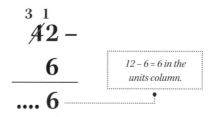

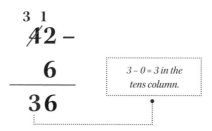

Here, when calculating 531 – 276 we have to trade in both the units and the tens column:

$$5\overset{2}{\cancel{3}}\overset{1}{1} -$$

$$276$$

$$...... \, 5$$

· We can't do 1 – 6 in the units column
· The 30 splits into 20 + 10
· 10 + 1 gives us 11 in the units column
· 11 – 6 = 5

$$\overset{4}{}\overset{12}{\cancel{5}}\overset{1}{\cancel{3}}1 -$$

$$276$$

$$... \, 55$$

· We can't do 2 – 7 in the tens column
· The 500 'decomposes' into 400 + 100
· The 100 trades into the tens column turning the 2 into a 12
· 12 – 7 = 5

$$^4 \overset{12}{\cancel{5}} \overset{1}{\cancel{3}} 1 -$$
$$276$$
$$\overline{255}$$

In the hundreds column $4 - 2 = 2$.

As you can see the numbers can get quite crowded up top here. Lots of practise should see your child avoid confusion.

$$531 - 276 = 255$$

2. Borrow and pay back

The second way of using the subtraction algorithm is called 'borrow and pay back' or 'equal addition'.

To understand this method you have to see that if you add the same amount to both terms in a subtraction, the answer remains the same.

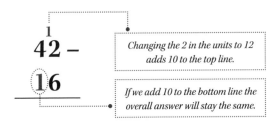

$$\overset{1}{4}2 -$$
$$\cancel{1}6$$

Changing the 2 in the units to 12 adds 10 to the top line.

If we add 10 to the bottom line the overall answer will stay the same.

$$\overset{1}{4}2 -$$
$$16$$
$$\overline{36}$$

$$12 - 6 = 6$$

$$4 - 1 = 3$$

Notice the 42 with the extra 1 is essentially 52. So we have rewritten $42 - 6 = 52 - 16 = 36$. This method got the same result as we did with the trading algorithm.

Let's use this method on the more difficult example of $531 - 276$:

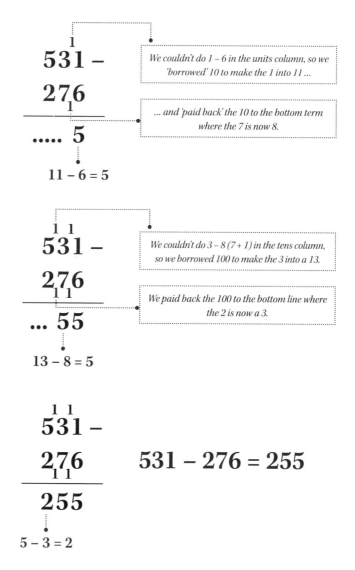

$$531 - 276 = 255$$

The reason this works is because by adding the same amount to both numbers, we're not changing the difference between them. If you and your child stand on the bottom step of a flight of ten stairs, the difference between your height and theirs is the same as when you are standing on the top step!

Now this stuff is not easy when your child first sees it. Perhaps it is even a bit murky for you? I can't stress how important it is for you to both be able to see why the algorithm works the way it does and to do enough examples so that the method becomes completely familiar. One missing 1, or an extra 1, can make your answer wrong.

Also check which of the methods your child has been taught, maybe both, before just jumping in with a subtraction algorithm.

Good luck!

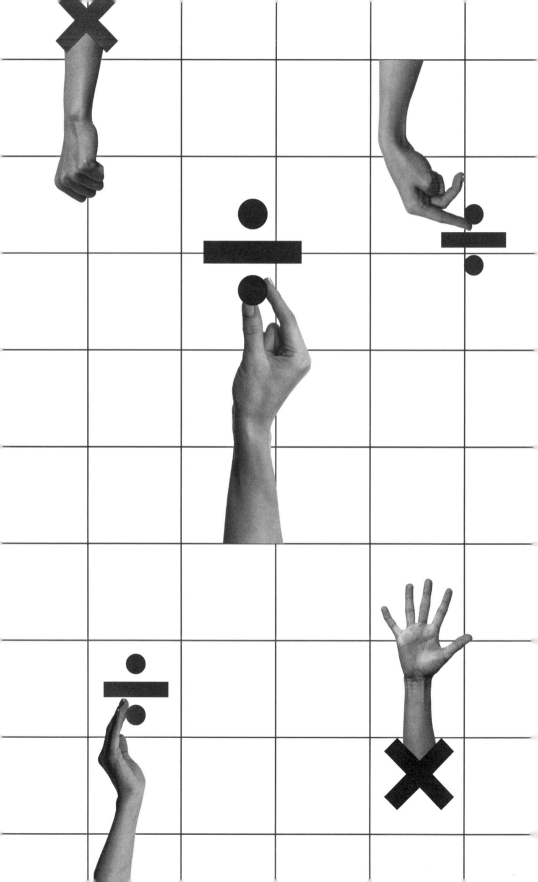

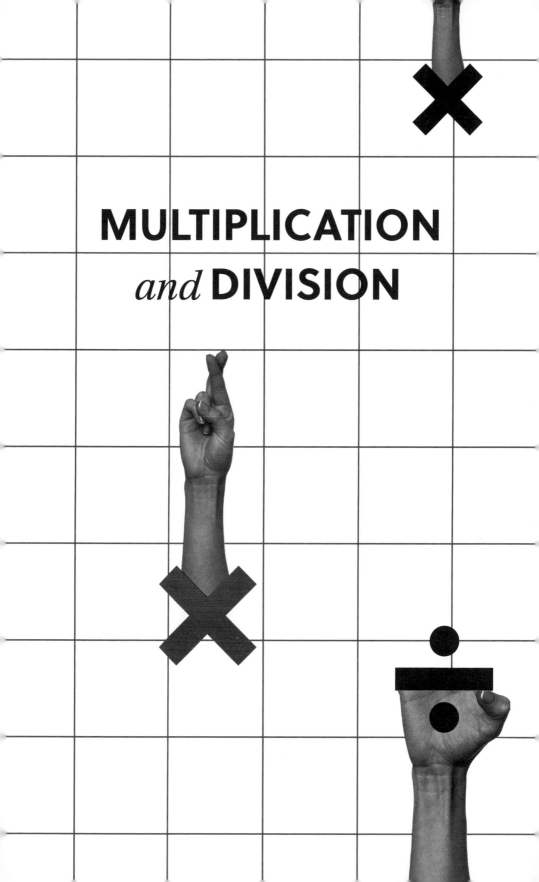

MULTIPLICATION
and DIVISION

Having learned how to count, add and subtract, the next stop on your child's arithmetic adventure is the world of multiplication and division.

How many stars are there?

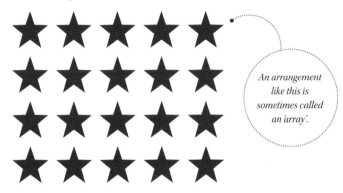

An arrangement like this is sometimes called an 'array'.

We can count them one by one and see that there are 20. Or we could look at the array as columns of 4 stars. Counting each column, we see there are 4, 8, 12, 16 ... 20 stars. There are 5 columns of 4 stars, so we could say '5 lots of 4 stars is 20 stars'.

This would work for stars, or oranges, or monkeys ... or anything.

We write this relationship between 5, 4 and 20 as the equation $5 \times 4 = 20$ and say '5 multiplied by 4 equals 20', or '5 times 4 equals 20' or, to save time, simply 'five fours are twenty'. If we are feeling fancy, we say the **'product' of 5 and 4 is 20.**

When things multiply together the answer is their 'product'.

Similarly, there are 4 rows of 5 stars, so we could just as easily get the equation $4 \times 5 = 20$.

So this is an important fact about multiplication: $5 \times 4 = 4 \times 5 = 20$. If we change the order of the terms we are multiplying the answer will be the same. You might remember from our chapter on addition that this property is called 'commutativity'. Addition and multiplication are commutative; subtraction and division are not.

Get your child to do the arrays needed to show that
$2 \times 4 = 4 \times 2 = 8$; $3 \times 6 = 6 \times 3 = 18$; $4 \times 7 = 7 \times 4 = 28$; $5 \times 5 = 25$

Multiplying more than two terms together

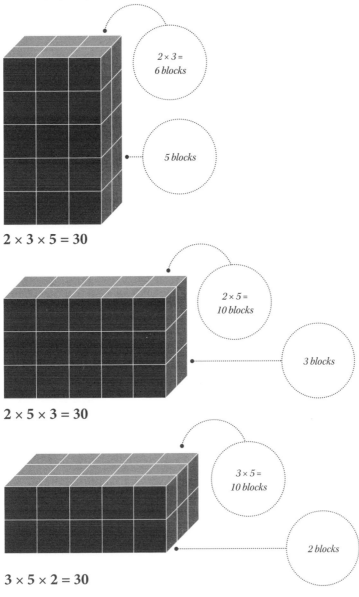

$2 \times 3 =$
6 blocks

5 blocks

2 × 3 × 5 = 30

$2 \times 5 =$
10 blocks

3 blocks

2 × 5 × 3 = 30

$3 \times 5 =$
10 blocks

2 blocks

3 × 5 × 2 = 30

And can you see from these diagrams that whichever way you look at the blocks, clearly the number of blocks doesn't change. So, by calculating the number of blocks on the top layer of the shape then multiplying by the height, you should be able to see that:

$$2 \times 3 \times 5 = 2 \times 5 \times 3 = 3 \times 5 \times 2 = 30$$

Can you and your child find all six ways you can write 2, 3 and 5 with multiplication to get the answer 30?

Multiplication tables

Practise counting by 3s. Can your child count 3, 6, 9, 12, 15, 18, 21, 24, 27, 30? They can start by looking at a list of numbers and jumping with their fingers. Then jump by sight alone. Then do it all in their mind. Hopefully it eventually becomes known off by heart.

Can you see that what they are doing here is calculating:

3
$3 + 3 = 6$
$3 + 3 + 3 = 9$
$3 + 3 + 3 + 3 = 12$
$3 + 3 + 3 + 3 + 3 = 15$

and so on. All the way up to:

$3 + 3 + 3 + 3 + 3 + 3 + 3 + 3 + 3 + 3 = 30$

To save writing out all of these addition signs, we can create a list.

3 is the same as $1 \times 3 = 3$, which we pronounce as 'one lot of three equals three', or 'one times three is three' or, to save time, 'one three is three'.

$3 + 3 = 6$ is the same as $2 \times 3 = 6$; 'two threes are six'
$3 + 3 + 3 = 9$ is the same as $3 \times 3 = 9$; 'three threes are nine'
$3 + 3 + 3 + 3 = 12$ is the same as $4 \times 3 = 12$; 'four threes are twelve'

And as we keep going we see that:

$$5 \times 3 = 15$$
$$6 \times 3 = 18$$
$$7 \times 3 = 21$$
$$8 \times 3 = 24$$
$$9 \times 3 = 27$$
$$10 \times 3 = 30$$

This list is called **the multiplication table for 3** or just our '**3 times table**'. We say the answers 3, 6, 9, 12... are the **multiples of 3**.

Counting by 2s, try and generate the multiplication table for 2. Then write out the times tables for 4s and 5s.

In fact, copy this whole grid out, and generate all the multiplication tables for 1 up to 10 (see following page).

×	1	2	3	4	5	6	7	8	9	10
1	1	2	3	4	5	6	7	8	9	10
2	2	4	6	8	10	12	14	16	18	20
3	3	6	9	**12**	15	18	21	24	27	30
4	4	8	**12**	16	20	24	28	32	36	40
5	5	10	15	20	25	30	35	**40**	45	50
6	6	12	18	24	30	36	42	48	54	60
7	7	14	21	28	35	42	49	56	63	70
8	8	16	24	32	**40**	48	56	64	72	80
9	9	18	27	36	45	54	63	72	81	90
10	10	20	30	40	50	60	70	80	90	100

It should be obvious in the diagram above that $3 \times 4 = 4 \times 3$ = 12, $8 \times 5 = 5 \times 8 = 40$ and so on. The diagonal e.g. $1 \times 1 = 1$, $5 \times 5 = 25$ and so on, contains the 'squares'. More on these bad boys later!

Do I just have to memorise these things?

Let's be honest here ... yes, you should. **You really should**, and so should the kiddies. Your child should be able to draw an array and understand what 6×7 means and why 6×7 = 42, but they should also read their times tables so many times these answers just come automatically.

I can't stress how important this is. Through all of primary school and high school, your child will do so much multiplication and other mathematics that requires multiplication that if they don't know their tables really well they will struggle. Even if they know them but it takes them a long time to remember 'seven eights are ... um ... er ... shhhh I've got this ... 56' they will be wasting a lot of time over the thousands of times they will multiply numbers together.

And when they move to other subjects, say, area, they may fully understand how to draw the diagram, how to label the sides; they may realise that we just remove the triangle from the bigger rectangle etc., but if at the end of the day they think $8 \times 6 = 40$, when in fact it is 48, they are stuffed! They will lose marks for things they actually understand because the basic arithmetic lets them down.

Take the time to burn the times tables deeply into your child's mind.

And for anyone thinking 'but memorising isn't learning, it's cheating!' Ask yourself this, every morning when you go to tie your shoes, do you stare at the laces thinking 'there has to be a way to secure these to my feet' ... no, you have learned by rote how to tie your shoelaces and if you hadn't you'd waste minutes, perhaps hours every day trying to do it.

It's the same with making bread. I'm sure your local baker is intelligent enough that if you left them alone in a room with some warm water, olive oil, a variety of flours and some raisins, they would, eventually, create an incredible artisan loaf of sourdough. But sweet bippy, that's a silly way to do things as opposed to learning the recipe by heart and following it every day.

I know I'm stretching the point a bit, but rote learning gets a bum rap and I'm doing my bit to change that.

When it comes to committing times tables to memory, here's a handy tip that I used with my daughters that really seemed to help.

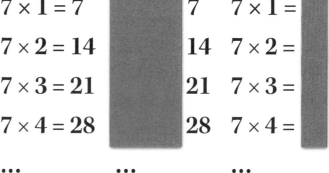

$$7 \times 1 = 7$$
$$7 \times 2 = 14$$
$$7 \times 3 = 21$$
$$7 \times 4 = 28$$

...

7    $7 \times 1 =$
14   $7 \times 2 =$
21   $7 \times 3 =$
28   $7 \times 4 =$

...   ...

In my experience, the equations $6 \times 9 = 54$ and $7 \times 8 = 56$ can really take a while to sink into the memory of a child. One cute thing to remember is that $56 = 7 \times 8$ reads as 5 6 7 8!

Say you're trying to memorise the seven times table. Rather than reading out the entire table time after time, as appears above on the left, sometimes cover up the equations and just let the child read the answer, doing the equations from memory. Then cover up the answers and just let them read the equations but quote the answers from memory. Mixing it up like this might make it sink in a bit quicker ... happy rote learning.

It's not surprising that it's the bigger numbers on the tables that cause the most trouble. Make sure your child is rock solid on the 6, 7, 8 and 9 times tables.

What about multiplying numbers bigger than 10?

For some students (and quite a few parents!), multiplication is all fine and dandy up to and including our ten times tables. But when we move to multiplying numbers greater than 10, the shutters go up, the fog descends, and we enter the land of 'I don't really understand it, but my best guess is sort of this'.

Let's put that to bed here and now by exploring the multiplication of larger numbers.

When one number is bigger than 10

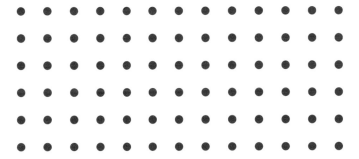

If you take the time to count the dots above, you should be able to see that $13 \times 6 = 78$.

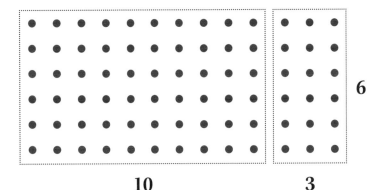

10   3

6

And if we break the dots into two blocks like this we can see that:

$$13 \times 6 = (10 \times 6) + (3 \times 6) = 60 + 18 = 78$$

The multiplication algorithm that your child will learn follows exactly the same logic; it just does it all with numbers not dots. Do you agree we could write this as:

$$
\begin{array}{r}
13 \times \\
6 \\
\hline
18 \\
60 \\
\hline
78
\end{array}
$$

- $18 \cdots\!\cdot 6 \times 3$
- $60 \cdots\!\cdot 6 \times 10$
- $78 \cdots\!\cdot$ **add 18 + 60 using the addition algorithm**

and get the same result?

Do a few examples until this sinks in. I recommend for the first few you draw the dots and do everything we have done here. Convince yourself that:

$14 \times 7 = 98$
$16 \times 6 = 96$
$17 \times 9 = 153$
and $26 \times 8 = 208$
(Note: for the last example, in the dots diagram just break the 26 dots into 20 and 6.)

When both numbers are bigger than 10

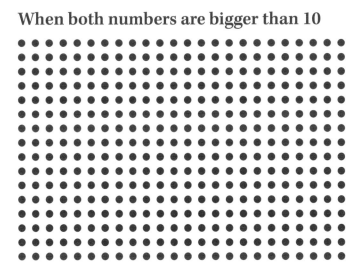

This confronting diagram is just another multiplication array. Exactly like the one we started this chapter with. The only difference is that while we started with 5 × 4, we have now graduated to 24 × 16. Don't be scared – be flattered!

In the same way that our first array convinced us that 5 × 4 = 20, this array proves convincingly that 24 × 16 = 384 (no need to count the dots; the wonderful Janine Sprakel who helped me with this book has already done exactly that!).

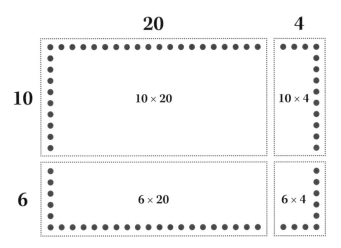

But if we look at the dots this way we can see that 24×16 = $(10 \times 20) + (6 \times 20) + (10 \times 4) + (6 \times 4) = 200 + 120 + 40 + 24 = 384$.

And if we wanted we could have written it this way:

$$
\begin{array}{r}
24 \times \\
16 \\
\hline
24 \\
120 \\
40 \\
200 \\
\hline
384
\end{array}
$$

24 .... 6×4

120 .... 6×20

40 .... 10×4

200 .... 10×20

384 .... using the addition algorithm

Again, take a few moments to look back at this and for it to make sense. Because from here to the sometimes 'dreaded' multiplication algorithm is just a short step.

The actual multiplication algorithm

We have done these examples in longhand so you realise what we are doing when we use the multiplication algorithm. It is not some crazy new way to do mathematics. It just speeds up exactly the same process we have been doing in these last two examples.

What we just did this way:

$$13 \times \cdots\cdots 10 + 3$$

$$\underline{6}$$

$$18 \cdots\cdots 6 \times 3$$

$$\underline{60 \cdots\cdots 6 \times 10}$$

$$78$$

The algorithm shortens to this:

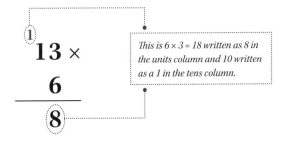

¹
$$13 \times$$
$$\underline{6}$$
$$8$$

This is 6 × 3 = 18 written as 8 in the units column and 10 written as a 1 in the tens column.

1
$$13 \times$$
$$\underline{6}$$
$$78$$

6 × 10 = 60, which would be a 6 in the tens column. But we have the 10 from the 18 as well. Adding that gives us 70, or 7 in the tens column.

If you're still a bit stuck, do some more examples of a two-digit number multiplied by a single digit until you can see how the 6 × 1 + 1 = 7 step here is the same as adding the tens column in the longer version we started with.

That last step again:

$$13 \times$$

$$6$$

$$\overline{78}$$

> *10 + 60 = 1 + 6 in the tens column =*
> *70 = 7 in the tens column.*

$$^{1}13 \times$$

$$6$$

$$\overline{78}$$

> *The multiplication algorithm just*
> *speeds up this process.*

Let's look at the two methods, side by side:

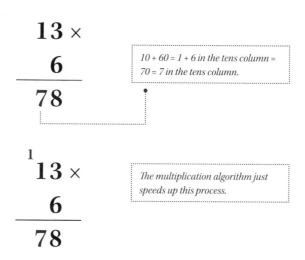

$$6 \times 8 = 48$$

$$26 \times$$

$$8$$

$$\overline{48} \cdots \cdot 8 \times 6$$

$$\underline{160} \cdots \cdot 8 \times 20$$

$$208$$

$$^{4}26 \times$$

$$8$$

$$\overline{208}$$

$$8 \times 2 + 4 = 20$$

$$4 + 16 = 20$$

If our product is large enough we might step out of the tens column into the hundreds column as we did here.

Multiplying two 2-digit numbers together using the algorithm

Let's start with an easier case, where one of the numbers is in the teens. In fact, let's go back to our old buddy 24 × 16.

$$
\begin{array}{r}
24 \times \\
16 \\
\hline
24 \\
120 \\
40 \\
200 \\
\hline
384
\end{array}
$$

- 24 ⋯⋯ · 6×4
- 120 ⋯⋯ · 6×20
- 40 ⋯⋯ · 10×4
- 200 ⋯⋯ · 10×20

$$
\begin{array}{r}
{}^{2}24 \times \\
16 \\
\hline
144 \\
\ldots
\end{array}
$$

144 ⋯⋯ · **6×24 using the multiplication algorithm**

24 ×

16
_____

144

0 ·········· *We have calculated 6 × 24; we still need to add 10 × 24 to get 16 × 24.*

10 × 24 will obviously end in a zero, so write it here.

24 ×

16
_____

144

240 ············ · 1 × 24 = 24 so
10 × 24 = 240

24 ×

16
_____

144

240
_____

384 ············· · **using the addition algorithm**

The only other example to consider here is when both two-digit numbers are a bit bigger so we can't just say '10 × 24 = 240' like we just did. The mathematics doesn't change here. But the examples are larger so it is easier to make a mistake. Practise lots of these ... please!

Here's 53 × 65 done the long way ...

$$^1\!53 \times$$
$$65$$
$$\overline{}$$

15	5×3
250	5×50
180	60×3
3000	60×50
3445	using the addition algorithm

... and by the multiplication algorithm. When we get to the 6 in the tens column, we use the multiplication algorithm again to work out 6 × 53. The zero written in red turns 6 × 53 into 60 × 53.

$$^1\!53 \times$$
$$65$$

| 265 | multiplication algorithm for 5×53 |
| . . . . | |

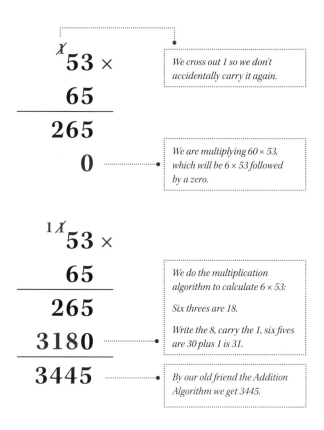

$\cancel{1}53 \times$

65

265

0

We cross out 1 so we don't accidentally carry it again.

We are multiplying 60 × 53, which will be 6 × 53 followed by a zero.

$^1\cancel{1}53 \times$

65

265

3180

3445

We do the multiplication algorithm to calculate 6 × 53:

Six threes are 18.

Write the 8, carry the 1, six fives are 30 plus 1 is 31.

By our old friend the Addition Algorithm we get 3445.

Extension!

To infinity (well, 100) and beyond

If you are comfortable with the multiplication algorithm and what it actually does, you should be able to see how we extend it to multiply larger numbers.

This is not on the primary school syllabus, so don't worry if it is a step too far for your child. But here it is anyway.

To multiply 256 × 314 we just add another row to the algorithm. It immediately contains two zeroes because we are multiplying by hundreds.

$$
\begin{array}{r}
\overset{2\ \ 2}{256} \times \\
\underset{1\ \ 1\ \ 1}{314} \\
\hline
1024 \\
2560 \\
76800 \\
\hline
80384 \\
\hline
\end{array}
$$

10 × 256 is

·1 × 256 and a 0

·300 × 256 is

3 × 256 and
two zeroes

Extension!

Two supercool long multiplication families

The following patterns aren't actually that hard to replicate if you are solid with the long multiplication algorithm. Have a crack. They rock.

$$1 \times 1 = 1$$
$$11 \times 11 = 121$$
$$111 \times 111 = 12321$$
$$1111 \times 1111 = 1234321$$
$$11111 \times 11111 = 123454321$$
$$111111 \times 111111 = 12345654321$$
$$1111111 \times 1111111 = 1234567654321$$
$$11111111 \times 11111111 = 123456787654321$$
$$1111111111 \times 111111111 = 12345678987654321$$

$$1 \times 9 + 2 = 11$$
$$12 \times 9 + 3 = 111$$
$$123 \times 9 + 4 = 1111$$
$$1234 \times 9 + 5 = 11111$$
$$12345 \times 9 + 6 = 111111$$
$$123456 \times 9 + 7 = 1111111$$
$$1234567 \times 9 + 8 = 11111111$$
$$12345678 \times 9 + 9 = 111111111$$
$$123456789 \times 9 + 10 = 1111111111$$

Division

Division and multiplication are intimately related. You can think of them as 'opposites' of each other, though we mathematicians tend to use the word 'inverse'.

Division emerges naturally from multiplication.

This grid tells us that $3 \times 4 = 12$.

The same grid also shows us that

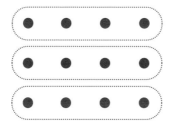

... if we break 12 up into groups of 4, we get exactly three of these groups.

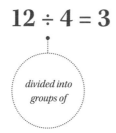

$$12 \div 4 = 3$$

divided into groups of

The official name for the division sign is the obelus and it was first used in 1659 by Swiss mathematician Johann Rahn in his book Teutsche Algebra. *Great stuff J-Dog.*

And we simplify this to 'twelve divided by four equals three'.

Looking at the same grid not as rows of 4 but as columns of 3 actually tells us two other things. It tells us that:

$$4 \times 3 = 12 \text{ and } 12 \div 3 = 4$$

So by thinking about a 3 by 4 grid of 12 dots, you should see that $12 = 3 \times 4$; $12 = 4 \times 3$; $12 \div 4 = 3$ and $12 \div 3 = 4$ are all essentially telling you the same thing.

We can also rearrange these dots into this shape grid:

And realise that $12 = 2 \times 6$; $12 = 6 \times 2$; $12 \div 2 = 6$ and $12 \div 6 = 2$.

We could also make a single row of 12 dots and observe that $12 = 1 \times 12 = 12 \times 1$; $12 \div 12 = 1$ and $12 \div 1 = 12$.

The fact that multiplication and division are so intimately related is yet another reason for children to learn their times tables off by heart. If you know instantly that $6 \times 7 = 42$, it is pretty easy to see that $42 \div 6 = 7$. But if the whole 6×7 thing is painful or worse, a guess, what chance does your child have of using the inverse process of division?

Test your child on division LOTS

Go back to our multiplication table and pick a random square.

Say you chose the number 28.

×	1	2	3	4	5	6	7	8	9	10
1	1	2	3	4	5	6	7	8	9	10
2	2	4	6	8	10	12	14	16	18	20
3	3	6	9	12	15	18	21	24	27	30
4	4	8	12	16	20	24	28	32	36	40
5	5	10	15	20	25	30	35	40	45	50
6	6	12	18	24	30	36	42	48	54	60
7	7	14	21	28	35	42	49	56	63	70
8	8	16	24	32	40	48	56	64	72	80
9	9	18	27	36	45	54	63	72	81	90
10	10	20	30	40	50	60	70	80	90	100

The number 28 is here in this row and column because
$4 \times 7 = 28$.

If your child knows this, they should be able to tell you
$28 \div 7 = 4$ and $28 \div 4 = 7$.

What about when division isn't clean?

By now you should look at this grid of 28 stars and realise it
is telling you that:

$28 \div 4 = 7.$

But this grid shows us that 30 stars cannot be neatly broken up into exact groups of 4. We see here that:

30 ÷ 4 = 7 with 2 stars remaining

We say '30 divided by 4 is 7 **remainder** 2'.

If 5 children divide 17 chocolates equally between them are there any left over?

The multiples of 5 on our five times table are 5, 10, 15, 20, 25 and so on.

The closest we can get to 17 is 5 × 3 = 15.

So there are 17 chocolates and 17 ÷ 5 = 3 remainder 2. Each child will get three chocolates and there will be 2 left over.

The official terms for the numbers and notation used here are as follows:

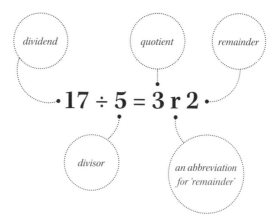

Children who excel at primary school mathematics know the table on page 69 and the multiplication and division results it contains as naturally as children who are good at spelling know their ABCs. **Thoroughly drilling these results into them is possibly the single best thing you can take from this whole book in terms of helping your child with primary school maths!**

The division algorithm

Just like we did with multiplication, when numbers get bigger and we move beyond our 10 × 10 multiplication grid, we have an algorithm to help us with division.

And just like we did with multiplication, it's really important to work a few examples longform first to understand what the algorithm is actually doing. It's not magic. It's not some higher form of mathematics; it is EXACTLY what we are doing longhand, just sped up.

Here's an example:

One school holiday, Ellie, Liv, Tai and Indi work incredibly hard helping a neighbour move house, spending days packing boxes and stacking them up. When it is all done, the grateful neighbour gives them $596 to share evenly. How much will they each get?

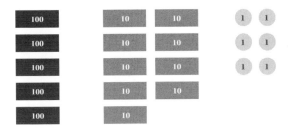

Here is the $596 grouped as 5 hundreds, 9 tens, and 6 ones.

The best we can do with five hundreds is to give them one each.

We have one hundred left over.

We consider this hundred as ten tens. We add it to the 9 tens we have already, getting 19 tens.

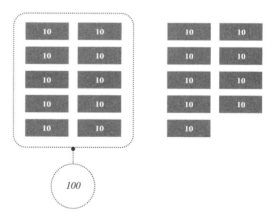

Dividing 19 tens between 4 people – they get 4 tens each. There are 3 tens left over.

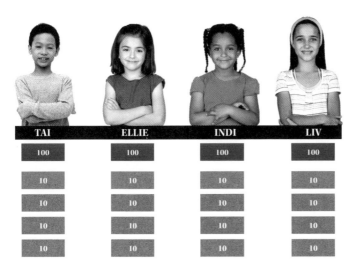

We think of these 3 tens as 30 units and add them to the 6 units we already have, getting 36 units.

36 units divided among 4 people is 9 units each.

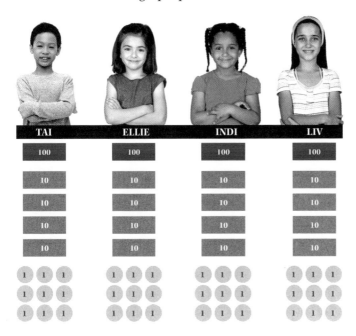

They get $149 each for their efforts.

Just like its good buddy the multiplication algorithm, the division algorithm simply makes this process quicker. The maths is exactly the same.

Look back over the workings on the previous pages and consider this algorithm:

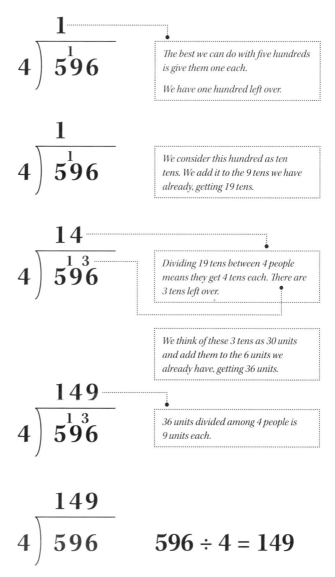

$$596 \div 4 = 149$$

If the divisor (in this case the 4) does not go perfectly into the dividend (in this case the 596) you simply get a remainder.

If instead of 596 ÷ 4 I had asked you 598 ÷ 4, you should see you would get exactly the same answer down to the very last step where we would have a reminder of 2.

$$149 \text{ r } 2$$
$$4 \overline{\smash{)}598}$$ $$38 \div 4 = 9 \text{ r } 2$$

Here is a special case to quickly note, but in truth it is no more difficult than what we have already done. At first it may be confusing that the divisor 7, is greater than the hundreds digit 5. No trouble there.

$$075 \text{ r } 4$$
$$7 \overline{\smash{)}529}$$

5 hundreds divided by 7 ... we can't divide 7 into 5, it's too big, so we just pass the 5 hundreds across into the tens column, giving 52 tens.

From there it's business as usual, 7 into 52 goes 7 remainder 3 and so on.

Convince yourself by the division algorithm that:

390 ÷ 4 = 97 r 2; 659 ÷ 8 = 82 r 3; 2317 ÷ 7 = 331 and 892 ÷ 6 = 148 r 4.

If any of these just won't come out correctly, maybe go back to the longhand like the example of the kids getting paid by their neighbour and see if you can get the correct answer.

Feel free to do hundreds more examples from your child's textbooks or online. Happy 'Division Algorithms'!

Back in my day (the old division algorithm that confuses some people)

One thing that confuses some parents at this stage of their child's maths journey is the feeling 'we did it differently back in my day'.

The truth is, 'you did – but really you didn't!'

Here's an example of the division that we did earlier alongside the 'long division' method parents may have done at school back in the day. If you look closely you will see they are essentially the same.

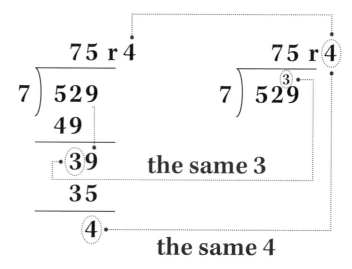

Italian or lattice method for multiplication

Sometimes in primary school, especially in extension programs, children encounter other algorithms or methods for multiplication. Lattice multiplication, sometimes called the Italian or Chinese method, is a particular favourite. Check it out with this example multiplying 63 × 285.

We start by writing 63 across the top and 285 down the side of the lattice. The top left square of the lattice is in the column labelled 6 and the row labelled 2, so in that square we write the product of 6 × 2 (12) with the digits split by the diagonal.

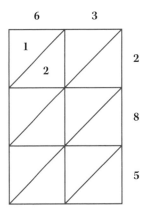

continue →

Extension continued!

We can fill up all the squares this way, noting that if the number for one of the squares is less than 10, just write a 0 in the top half of the square, like I've shown here in **red**.

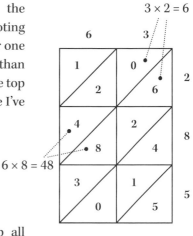

$3 \times 2 = 6$

$6 \times 8 = 48$

After we've filled up all the squares in the lattice, we add up the numbers along a diagonal and write that at the bottom of the diagonal. We start at the bottom-right diagonal, which is just one triangle, and work to the left, ending at the very top-left triangle. If the sum of a diagonal adds to more than 10, we write the value of the tens place at the bottom of the next diagonal and add it when we sum that diagonal.

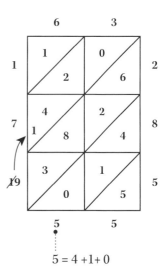

$5 = 4 + 1 + 0$

Numbers are added to the left and to the bottom of the grid, and the answer is the digits read down (on the left) and then across (on the bottom). So, as you see, 285 × 63 = 17,955.

You should be able to convince yourself that if you write 285 across the top and 63 down the side you'd still get the same answer.

That wasn't so bad was it?

We've got no idea who actually 'invented' lattice multiplication but we know that it was being used far and wide centuries ago. Famous lattice multipliers include:

- The Arab mathematician Ibn al-Banna' al-Marrakushi in his cracking read *Talkhis a'mal al-hisab* in the Maghreb (what is now north-west Africa) in the late thirteenth century;
- The Chinese mathematician Wu Jing in his *Jiuxhang Suanfa Bilei Daquan*, completed in 1450; and let's not forget;
- The anonymous English maths geek who wrote the Latin page-turner *Tractatus de minuits philosophicus et vulagribus* around 1300.

Extension!

Divisibility tests

When you are trying to factorise a number there are some handy little shortcuts that can speed things up a bit. They are known as **divisibility tests** and while students won't normally encounter them until year 7, they are great fun to show to younger students who really 'get' division.

2

It should be clear that any number that is divisible by 2 must finish in a 0, 2, 4, 6 or 8.

4

The number 100 is divisible by 4. So obviously 1000 is divisible by 4 and so is 10,000 and 100,000 and so on. So to check if a number is divisible by 4, we only have to look at the last two digits of the number and check if that two digit number is divisible by 4.

So 34,564 is divisible by 4 because 64 = 16 × 4. Similarly, 56,734,570 is not divisible by 4 because 70 ÷ 4 = 17 r 2.

8

Following a similar logic to the test for 4, because 1,000 is divisible by 8 (1000 = 125 × 8) we test for divisibility by 8 by testing the number formed by the last 3 digits of our number.

So 6,848 is divisible by 8 and 52,244 is not.

5

Thinking about counting by fives 5, 10, 15, 20, 25, 30... makes it obvious that a number that is divisible by 5 ends in a 0 or a 5.

3

This is where things get interesting! If a number is divisible by 3 the sum of its digits is also divisible by 3.

So 34,718 is not divisible by 3 (3 + 4 + 7 + 1 + 8 = 23) whereas 546,705 is (5 + 4 + 6 + 7 + 0 + 5 = 27 = 3 × 9).

9

The divisibility test for 9 is almost a copy of the test for 3. If the sum of the digits of a number is divisible by 9, the original number is divisible by 9.

So 6,723 is divisible by 9 (6 + 7 + 2 + 3 = 18 = 2 × 9) but 43,665 is not (4 + 3 + 6 + 6 + 5 = 24).

It's really important that once your child learns the divisibility rules for 3 and 9 they don't mistakenly think you can test for divisibility by 4 or 6 or 7, or similar, by adding up the digits. These tests only work for 3 and 9.

6

If a number is divisible by 6 then clearly it is divisible by 2 and by 3. To check for divisibility by 6, we apply the tests for divisibility by 2 and 3.

Extension continued!

These are the main divisibility rules that your child will meet in year 7. But in the spirit of giving you more, here are another couple.

7

Take your number, double the last digit of the number, drop that last digit and subtract the doubling from this new shortened number. If that number is divisible by 7, so was the original number. You may want to repeat this a few times. Huh? Clear as mud yeah? Let's check an example.

Is 315,861 divisible by 7?

315,861 – the last digit is 1, doubling that we get 2.

31,586 is the 315,861 with the last digit removed.

31,586 – 2 = 31,584 – subtracting the doubling from the shortened number.

We don't know off the top of our heads if 31,584 is divisible by 7 so let's do the process again.

$31{,}584 \rightarrow 2 \times 4 = 8 \rightarrow 3158 - 8 = 3150 \rightarrow 2 \times 0 = 0 \rightarrow 315 - 0 = 315 \rightarrow 2 \times 5 = 10 \rightarrow 31 - 10 = 21$ and $21 = 3 \times 7$ so 21 is divisible by 7, meaning that 315,861 is divisible by 7.

In fact, $315{,}861 = 7 \times 45{,}123$.

37

37 is a factor of 999, which gives it this beautiful property.

For any number with digits *abcde* ... take the first digit and add it to the fourth, in this case getting the number *bc(a+d)e* ... Keep doing this until you get a three digit number. If that final number is divisible by 37, the original number was ...

Again, best check out an example:

348,022 → adding the first digit (3) to the fourth digit (0) → 48,322 → add the 4 to the 2 → 8362 → add the 8 to the 2 → 370.

370 is clearly divisible by 37, so 348,022 is too.
(In fact, 348,022 = 37 × 9406.)

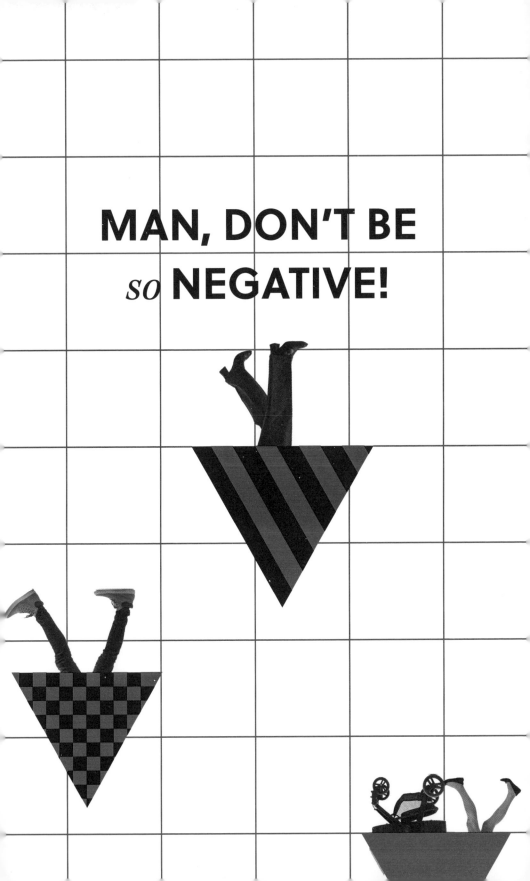

We met negative numbers in our chapter on addition and subtraction. But I'd like to take a closer look here. My wife Leah is pretty sharp and was a great help for her kids as they tackled primary school mathematics. But when I was preparing this book she was honest enough to admit to me that negative numbers and the way we do arithmetic with them really confused her.

So, let's take a deeper dive into this topic that, understandably, does freak some people out.

The guiding principle here, as it is so often in this book, is that you really are best to take it slowly, be comfortable with each step before moving forward, and truly understand how this all works. Don't commit things to memory that make no real sense to you. It pays in the long run.

Let's look again at the number line. It shows the counting numbers.

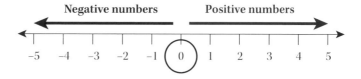

If we start at 0 and move to the right, we step through 1, 2, 3 and off we go. But if we step to the left of 0 we walk through the negative numbers –1, –2, –3 and so on. We pronounce these numbers 'minus one' or 'negative one', 'minus two', 'negative three' etc.

If I start at 0 and step two places to the right, I end up at 2.

If I did this three times in a row, I would step from 0 to 2, then to 4 and land on 6.

This shows us that 'three steps of two places each gives the same result as a single step from 0 to 6'. We write this as $3 \times 2 = 6$.

This is about as much as primary kids need to know, but if they (and you) are interested in knowing more, read on!

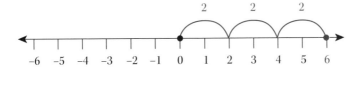

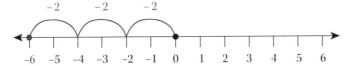

What if I start at 0 and move in the other direction? This means I step two places to the left. I would get to –2.

If I stepped 2 places to the left, three times in a row, I would go from 0 to –2, then to –4 and end up on –6.

So in exactly the same way as we say 3 × 2 = 6, we can write 3 × –2 = –6. Read this again and again until it makes complete sense.

So let's drill a bit further into these negative numbers. The following three diagrams should show you three different ways to think about negative 3.

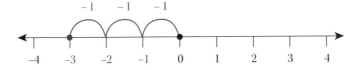

Firstly, by taking three steps to the left on the number line we see that 3 × –1 = –3.

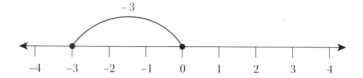

Secondly, by taking one step three places in the negative direction, we see that $-3 \times 1 = -3$.

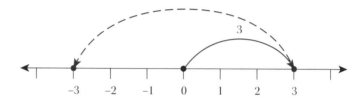

Finally, by stepping to positive 3, then flipping it to the negative side of the number line, we see that to get from 3 to –3 we just 'flip the direction'.

So if we start at 3 and 'flip the direction' we get exactly the same result as when we start with 3 and multiply by negative 1.

Multiplying by negative one just 'flips' a number around to the opposite side of 0 on the number line.

Similarly, consider the example from earlier of $3 \times -2 = -6$.

Look at all these different ways to get to –6 on the number line and see if the equations all make sense for you.

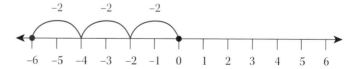

$$3 \times -2 = -6$$

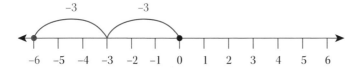

$$2 \times -3 = -6$$

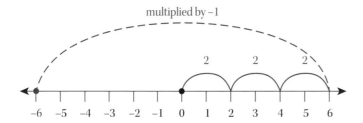

$$3 \times 2 \times -1 = -6$$

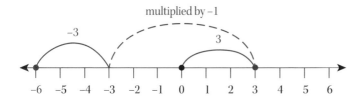

$$3 \times -1 \times 2 = -6$$

This last one may be a bit hard, but 3 × –1 gets us from + 3 to –3 and then multiplying by 2 just doubles our distance from 0 on the number line, hence the last jump from –3 to –6.

So in the same way that back on page 50 we saw that 2 × 3 × 5 = 2 × 5 × 3 = 3 × 5 × 2 etc., we can manipulate the 1, 2, 3 and negative sign and the answer remains the same.

So what happens if we 'flip' negative 3?

This stage of your mathematical journey, where we introduce multiple negatives, is where it gets really hard for some people to follow. Again, please make sure each step is completely clear before moving on.

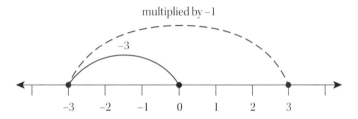

The diagram shows the only possible thing that can happen when we 'flip' −3 is that it becomes +3. But 'flipping' was the same as multiplying by negative 1.

$$So -3 \times -1 = 3$$

This confuses people when they first see it, but if you go back over the examples we have done in this section, hopefully it becomes clear that −3 × −1 must be equal to 3.

Another way that helps people sometimes is this. Say you were looking forward up a hill (call that the positive direction) and I asked you to turn 180 degrees. You are now looking down the hill (let's think of that as negative − no offence to downhill travel, I actually love it). What if I asked you to turn again? You'd be looking back uphill. So 'turn-turn' cancels itself out.

In the same way, if we start with 3 and 'flip' it around 0 to get −3, then clearly 'flip-flip' would start with 3 and end with 3. But 'flip' was just multiplying by −1, so:

$$-1 \times -1 \times 3 = -1 \times -3 = 3$$

Don't forget, adding negatives IS COMPLETELY DIFFERENT to multiplying by negatives.

Lots of people, once they've finally come on the journey to realising that $-2 \times -5 = 10$ will then see the equation:

$$-2 - 5 = ?$$

and, thinking 'two negatives has to give a positive', will give the answer 7, or perhaps even 10. No!

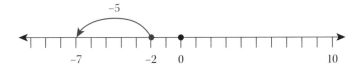

If we start at –2 and subtract 5, we step 5 places to the left on the number line and end up at –7. So $-2 - 5 = -7$. There was no multiplication involved here at all so 'negative multiplied by negative is positive' was never relevant.

Solve each of these equations. Don't forget that the order of operations applies (see our chapter on, you guessed it, 'Order of Operations').

$-2 - 3 + 5 = -5 + 5 = 0$

$3 \times -2 + 2 \times 5 = -6 + 10$ (we do the multiplications before the addition) $= 4$

$-3 \times (2 - 4) = -3 \times -2$ (brackets before multiplication) $= 6$ (negative multiplied by negative is positive).

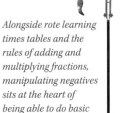

Alongside rote learning times tables and the rules of adding and multiplying fractions, manipulating negatives sits at the heart of being able to do basic mathematics.

Well done if you've made it this far. I hope it wasn't a negative experience. Negative! Get it ... oh, come on!

I'VE GOT
the POWER!

One subject that does tend to freak students out a bit, and maybe bring back some uncomfortable memories for parents, is powers.

It's a completely understandable reaction, the first time you see 2^3 or 3×10^5, you think 'okay, I was cool up until now, but if numbers are just going to start floating in the air like that ... I'm out'.

Well don't panic! Like a lot of mathematics, it looks a bit nastier than it really is.

It is important to understand that powers are **a shorthand way of writing**. They are used to save time. They are not new weird sorts of numbers or a different type of mathematics.

Let's start with the number 1 and double it a few times. Most youngsters have taken this a few steps – 1, 2, 4, 8, 16, 32, 64... and we can keep going ...128, 256, 512, 1024. Okay, Adam you've had your fun. Let's stop there.

So can you see that we reached the number 64 on this list by multiplying by 2 six times?

Can you see that $2 \times 2 \times 2 \times 2 \times 2 \times 2 = 64$? But mathematicians are inherently lazy creatures, so back in the early seventeenth century one of the all-time guns of mathematics and philosophy, René Descartes, set us on the path to powers notation.

Because $2 \times 2 \times 2 \times 2 \times 2 \times 2$ is six 2s multiplied together, we abbreviate this to 2^6. It's as simple as that. The weird and wonderful 6 floating up in the sky is just a note that we have multiplied six 2s together. We call this 'two to the power of six'.

6 is called the 'power' or the 'exponent' or the 'index' and tells us we are multiplying six 2s together = 64.

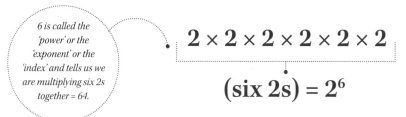

$$2 \times 2 \times 2 \times 2 \times 2 \times 2$$
$$(\text{six 2s}) = 2^6$$

Complete this table:

2	= 2	= 2^1
2 × 2	= 4	= 2^2
2 × 2 × 2	= 8	= 2^3
2 × 2 × 2 × 2	=16	=
	= 32	= 2^5
2 × 2 × 2 × 2 × 2 × 2	=	= 2^6

This works for all numbers, not just 2s.

Can you see that $3^2 = 3 \times 3 = 9$, $4^3 = 4 \times 4 \times 4 = 64$, and that $5^7 = 5 \times 5 \times 5 \times 5 \times 5 \times 5 \times 5 = 78{,}125$ (yes it's fine if you needed a calculator for that one).

Squares and cubes

For the smaller powers of 2 and 3, we use special terms that come from geometry. For example, we call 5^2 'five squared' and 7^3 'seven cubed'. Here's the reason why:

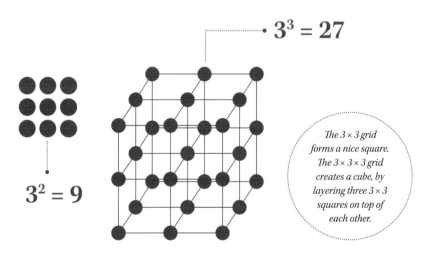

$$3^3 = 27$$

$$3^2 = 9$$

The 3 × 3 grid forms a nice square. The 3 × 3 × 3 grid creates a cube, by layering three 3 × 3 squares on top of each other.

A special case – the powers of 10

Because of the special role 10 plays in our number system, it is very important to understand the powers of 10.

Complete this table:

10	= 10	= ten	$= 10^1$
10 × 10	= 100	= one hundred	$= 10^2$
10 × 10 × 10	= 1000	= one thousand	$= 10^3$
10 × 10 × 10 × 10	= 10000	= ten thousand	$= 10^4$
10 × 10 × 10 × 10 × 10	= 100,000	= one hundred thousand	$= 10^5$
10 × 10 × 10 × 10 × 10 × 10	= 1,000,000	= one million	$= 10^6$
10 × 10 × 10 × 10 × 10 × 10 × 10	=	= ten million	$= 10^7$
10 × 10 × 10 × 10 × 10 × 10 × 10 × 10	= 100,000,000	= one hundred million	=
	= 1,000,000,000	= one billion	$= 10^9$

Perfect example!

Can you see that for $10^6 = 10 \times 10 \times 10 \times 10 \times 10 \times 10 = 1,000,000 =$ one million, the power of 6 corresponds **exactly** to the number of zeroes after the 1? Look back at the table until this fact is obvious for all of the numbers on the table. Your child should be able to look at a number like 10^4 and instantly think 'okay, it's a power of 10, the exponent is 4 ... so that's one followed by four 0s ... 10,000 ... ten thousand'.

Multiples of powers

So because powers like 10^2 are just a number ($10^2 = 100$) we can do all the fun things to it that we could do to any other numbers.

We can add and subtract them:

$$2^4 + 3^2 = 16 + 9 = 25$$
$$7^2 - 3^4 = 49 - 81 = -32$$
$$10^2 - 4^3 + 5^2 = 100 - 64 + 25 = 61$$

And importantly, we can multiply them:

$$\text{So, } 3 \times 10^5 = 3 \times 10{,}000 = 30{,}000$$
$$\text{and } 2^3 \times 5^2 = 8 \times 25 = 200$$

With powers of 10 we often go back the other way:

$$700{,}000 = 7 \times 10^5 \text{ and } 12{,}000{,}000{,}000 =$$
$$12 \times 1{,}000{,}000{,}000 = 12 \times 10^9$$

I hope I've shown you that powers are not all that scary. Just take your time, remember what they really mean and do LOTS of examples. Good luck, all power to you!

Extension!

Zenzi frenzy

Can you see from counting back from our table on page 95, that if $2^3 = 8$ and $2^2 = 4$ and $2^1 = 2$ it would make sense that $2^0 = 1$? Well, it does. In fact, $10^0 = 1$, as does 3^0, 4^0, in fact any number to the zero (except 0^0, which we explain later has no definition). You won't see this until high school, but feel free to freak your friends out with it today!

Silly side note

Allow me to introduce one of the coolest and least usable words in the English language. **Robert Recorde** was a Welsh mathematician in the 1500s who invented the equals sign that we use today.

In the same book we first met '=', the 1557 classic, *The Whetstone of Whitte*, he used the word **zenzizenzizenzic** to describe 'the square of squares squarely'.

Huh, Bob? Say that again.

Start with 3; square it to get $3 \times 3 = 3^2$; square the square to get $3 \times 3 \times 3 \times 3 = 3^4$; and this number squarely is $3 \times 3 \times 3 \times 3 \times 3 \times 3 \times 3 \times 3 = 3^8$.

So the next time your maths teacher drops a reference to an 8th power, e.g. 5^8, you can quickly reply 'Ah ... I think you mean the zenzizenzizenzic of 5', mic drop – out!

Like I said – very cool ... and almost entirely unusable!

zenzizenzizenzic

IN MEMORY OF
ROBERT RECORDE,
THE EMINENT MATHEMATICIAN,
WHO WAS BORN AT TENBY, CIRCA 1510.
TO HIS GENIUS WE OWE THE EARLIEST
IMPORTANT ENGLISH TREATISES ON
ALGEBRA, ARITHMETIC, ASTRONOMY, AND GEOMETRY;
HE ALSO INVENTED THE SIGN OF
EQUALITY = NOW UNIVERSALLY ADOPTED
BY THE CIVILIZED WORLD.

ROBERT RECORDE
WAS COURT PHYSICIAN TO
KING EDWARD VI. AND **QUEEN MARY.**
HE DIED IN LONDON.
1558.

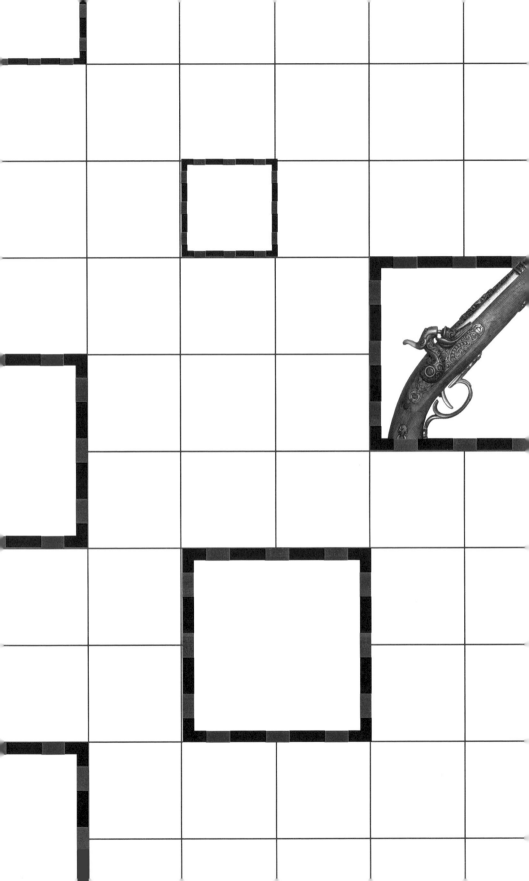

ALL'S SQUARE
in LOVE *and* WAR

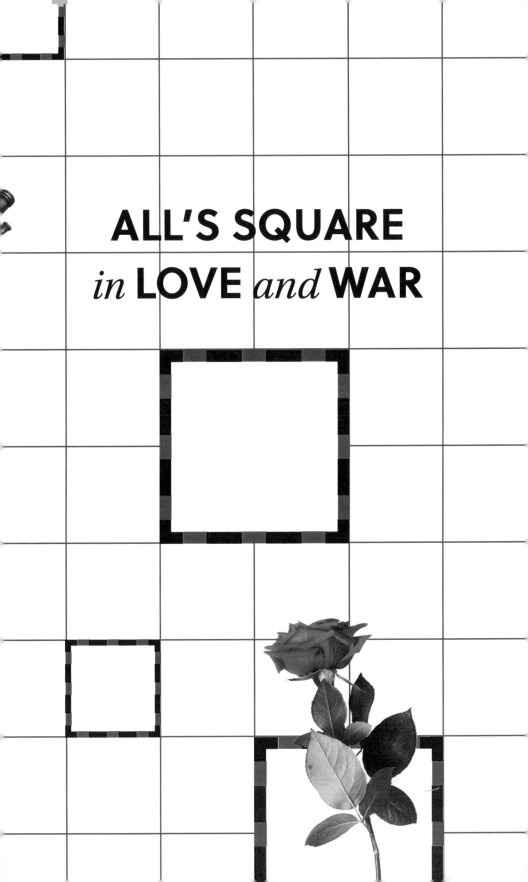

We mentioned on page 95 that when we multiply a number by itself, we get its **square**. This is a term that makes sense geometrically.

4 squared = 16 describes the 16 dots we see in a 4 × 4 square.

Similarly, when we describe 5 × 5 × 5 as 'five cubed', it perfectly describes the number of dots in the cube we obtain by stacking five 5 × 5 squares on top of each other.

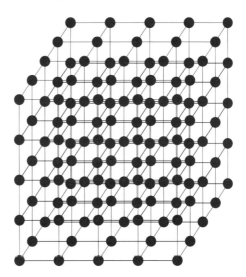

Primary students should be able to quote immediately all the single-digit squares; they are just part of the times tables after all! And students who are really crushing it will also know the first few cubes by sight.

$$1^3 = 1, 2^3 = 8, 3^3 = 27, 4^3 = 64 \text{ and } 5^3 = 125.$$

Now, if we can square 4 to get 16, then surely we can 'unsquare' 16 and get back to 4. The reverse of squaring (we fancy pants maths nerds say 'the inverse operation', but 'reverse' will do) is called **taking the square root.**

So, because we know that $4^2 = 16$ we can say that $\sqrt{16} = 4$.

Don't be freaked out by this – it's just a piece of notation representing 'square root' – here, we have 'the square root of 16 equals 4'.

$$So, 1^2 = 1 \times 1 = 1 \text{ and } \sqrt{1} = 1$$

$$2^2 = 2 \times 2 = 4 \text{ and } \sqrt{4} = 2$$

Get your child to complete this table of squares and cubes and their roots:

$$3^2 = 3 \times 3 = \underline{\quad} \text{ and } \sqrt{\underline{\quad}} = 3$$

$$\underline{\quad}^2 = 4 \times 4 = \underline{\quad} \text{ and } \sqrt{16} = 4$$

$$\underline{\quad}^2 = \underline{\quad} \times \underline{\quad} = \underline{\quad} \text{ and } \sqrt{25} = 5$$

$$6^2 = \underline{\quad} \times \underline{\quad} = \underline{\quad} \text{ and } \sqrt{\underline{\quad}} = \underline{\quad}$$

$$\underline{\quad}^2 = \underline{\quad} \times \underline{\quad} = \underline{\quad} \text{ and } \sqrt{\underline{\quad}} = 7$$

$$\underline{\quad}^2 = 8 \times 8 = \underline{\quad} \text{ and } \sqrt{\underline{\quad}} = \underline{\quad}$$

$$\underline{\quad}^2 = \underline{\quad} \times \underline{\quad} = \underline{\quad} \text{ and } \sqrt{81} = \underline{\quad}$$

$$10^2 = \underline{\quad} \times \underline{\quad} = \underline{\quad} \text{ and } \sqrt{\underline{\quad}} = \underline{\quad}$$

This notation, pronounced 'the cubed root of 1', reverses the process of cubing, just like taking the square root undoes squaring.

$$1^3 = 1 \times 1 \times 1 \text{ and } \sqrt[3]{1} = 1$$

The 3 attached to the root sign here is very important. It tells us we are taking the cube root NOT the square root.

$$2^3 = 2 \times 2 \times 2 = 8 \text{ and } \sqrt[3]{8} = 2$$

$$3^3 = 3 \times 3 \times 3 = \underline{\quad} \text{ and } \sqrt[3]{\underline{\quad}} = 3$$

$$\underline{\quad}^3 = 4 \times 4 \times 4 = \underline{\quad} \text{ and } \sqrt[3]{64} = \underline{\quad}$$

$$5^3 = \underline{\quad} \times \underline{\quad} \times \underline{\quad} = \underline{\quad} \text{ and } \sqrt[3]{\underline{\quad}} = \underline{\quad}$$

$$\underline{\quad}^3 = 10 \times 10 \times 10 = \underline{\quad} \text{ and } \sqrt[3]{\underline{\quad}} = \underline{\quad}$$

Extension!

Circular square

Take the number 76 and square it. By the multiplication algorithm (page 58), can you see that $76^2 = 5776$. Because the square of 76 ends in the number 76 itself, we call 76 a **circular number** (or **automorphic** if you're really trying to impress someone!). Apart from the obvious examples of 0 and 1, there are 3 more circular numbers that are less than 30. Find them.

Answer: 5, 6 and 25

Another extension!

That's irrational

What about square roots that aren't whole numbers?

We saw that $3^2 = 9$ and $4^2 = 16$ and therefore $\sqrt{9} = 3$ and $\sqrt{16} = 4$. Using a calculator will show you that $3.5^2 = 3.5 \times 3.5 = 12.25$. So there must be a number between 3 and 3.5 that squares to give us 10. Let's try and find that number, which of course is $\sqrt{10}$.

$3.1^2 = 9.61$, so we need a number greater than 3.1. $3.2^2 = 10.24$ so $\sqrt{10}$ is greater than 3.1 but less than 3.2. Let's go halfway between:

$3.15^2 = 9.9225$, so $\sqrt{10}$ lies between 3.15 and 3.2.

Keep trying with your calculator and see to how many decimal places you can close in on $\sqrt{10}$.

If you're super keen, you might have gone as far as $\sqrt{10} = 3.16227766$ but you are not finished! In fact you will NEVER get an exact decimal for $\sqrt{10}$. The decimal expansion of $\sqrt{10}$ never ends! More about these amazing numbers, called irrational numbers, in high school.

Yet another extension!

Ain't dat the trooth

Can fractions have square roots?

Well, why not?

To square 4 we multiplied 4 × 4 = 16. And from that we know $\sqrt{16} = 4$.

We can multiply fractions by themselves too.

If you understand that $\frac{2}{3} \times \frac{2}{3} = \frac{4}{9}$ then you should also be able to see that $\sqrt{\frac{4}{9}} = \frac{2}{3}$.

Similarly, $\sqrt{\frac{1}{9}} = \frac{1}{3}$; $\sqrt{\frac{64}{25}} = \frac{8}{5}$; $\sqrt{2\frac{1}{4}} = \sqrt{\frac{9}{4}} = \frac{3}{2}$; and $\sqrt[3]{\frac{8}{27}} = \frac{2}{3}$.

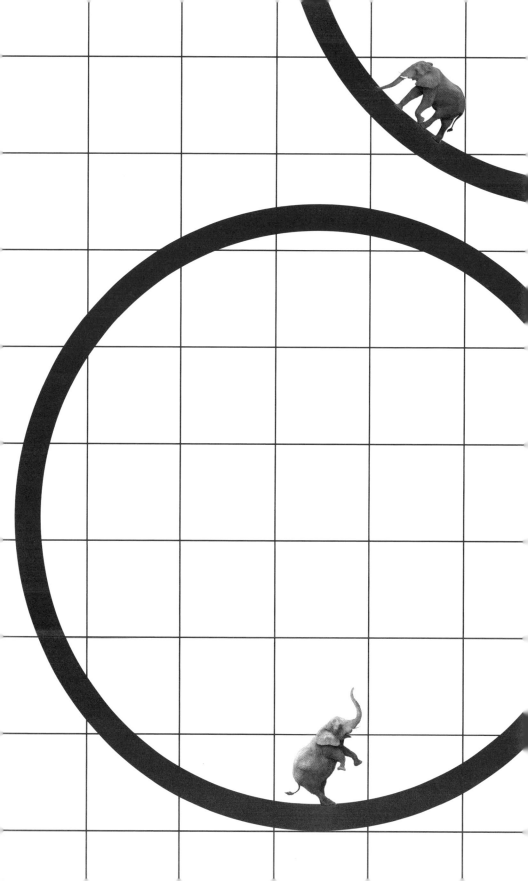

NAMING
massive NUMBERS

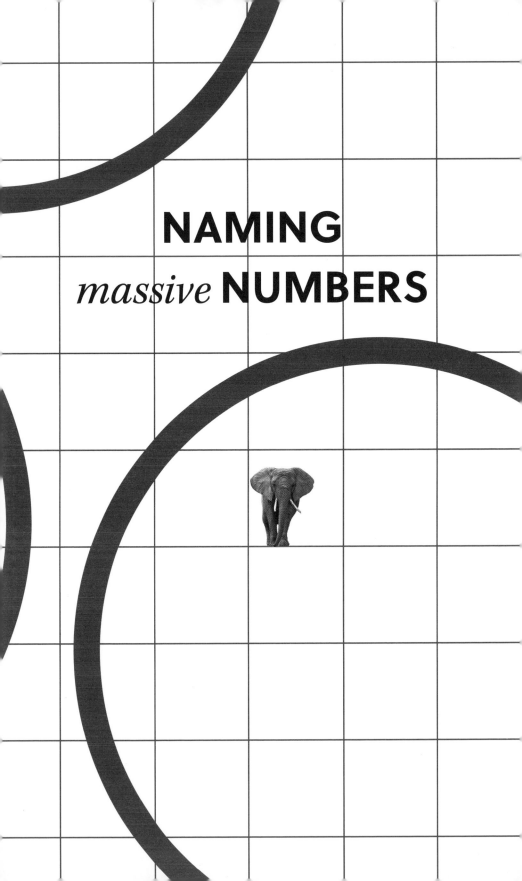

The best way to understand how to pronounce large numbers is to get right down to it and pronounce some big numbers. Okay – perhaps a quick style guide is needed.

We pronounce the number 2847 as 'two thousand, eight hundred and forty-seven' and you can see the names of the places that each digit occupies listed here:

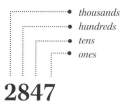

2847

If we add another digit, say a 5, in front of this number, the 5 is sitting in the 'tens of thousands' place. But we don't say 'five tens of thousands, two thousand, eight hundred and forty-seven'. We group the ten thousands and thousands as a two-digit number, in this case 52, and pronounce it 'fifty-two thousand, eight hundred and forty-seven'.

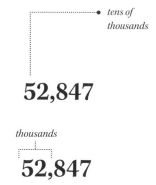

52,847

thousands

52,847

This process of grouping keeps on going as numbers get larger. A few examples are best here.

Meet 'six hundred and fifty-two thousand, eight hundred and forty-seven'.

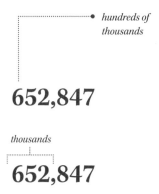

And now for the millions. We stop grouping thousands once we reach hundreds of thousands. We bracket the millions separately.

Meet 'six million, six hundred and fifty-two thousand, eight hundred and forty-seven' and watch as we now group the millions in introducing her big sister: 'thirty-six million, six hundred and fifty-two thousand, eight hundred and forty-seven'.

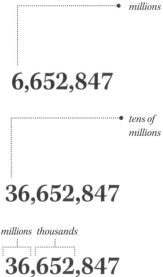

And finally, 'one hundred and thirty-six million, six hundred and fifty-two thousand, eight hundred and forty-seven'.

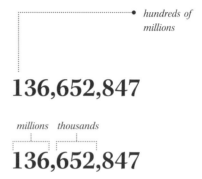

hundreds of millions

136,652,847

millions   *thousands*

136,652,847

As numbers get larger we keep grouping in up to threes: the billions and trillions, quadrillions and quintillions. I could go on all day, but with this being a book for primary school kids, I should really leave it there. Happy counting.

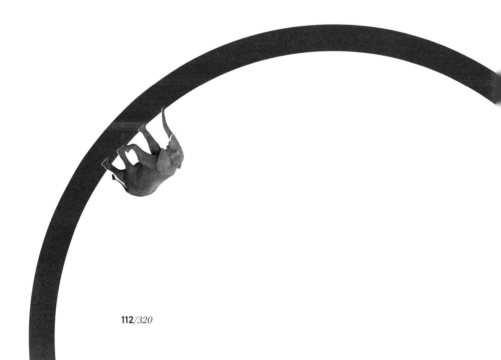

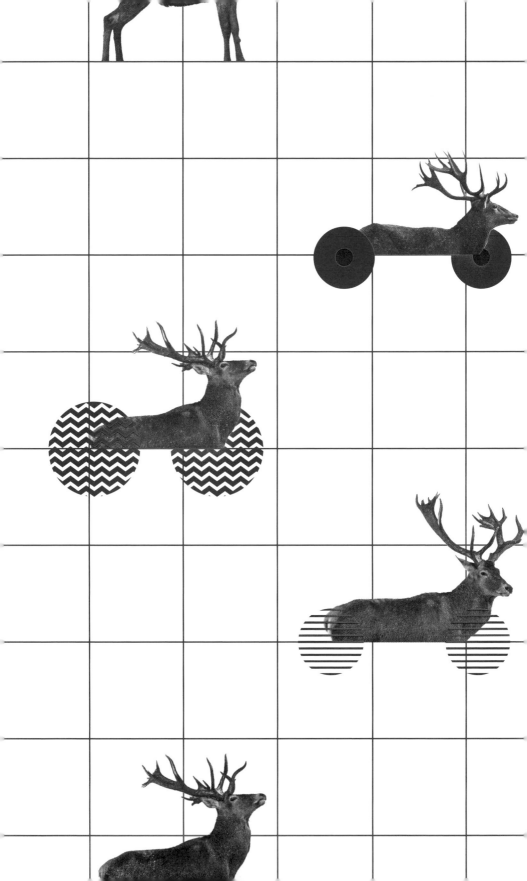

ORDER *of* OPERATIONS

Every now and then the internet 'melts down' when someone tweets or posts to Instagram something along the lines of:

'Just spent two hours arguing with my daughter about the answer to this ... please help:

$$4 - 4 \times 4 - 4$$

I say it is –4, she says it is –16. We can't both be right!'

The discussion goes wild for a few hours, people get very emotional, the option of 0 gathers some support, some start shouting BODMAS, BIDMAS or PEMDAS ... then we all go back to the big stories, like 'What is it with Taylor Swift's new haircut?'

But it is worth asking, what is $4 - 4 \times 4 - 4$, because it teaches us a very important rule in mathematics.

At first glance, there are probably three different ways you could attempt this question:

1. Just read it left to right:

$$4 - 4 \times 4 - 4 = 0 \times 4 - 4 = 0 - 4 = -4$$

2. Do all the minuses first, then the multiplication:

$$4 - 4 \times 4 - 4 = 0 \times 0 = 0$$

$$4 - 4 = 0$$

3. Do the multiplication first then the minuses:

$$4 - 4 \times 4 - 4 = 4 - 16 - 4 = -16$$

$$4 \times 4 = 16$$

Three different methods – three different answers.

Clearly, the order we perform the subtractions and the multiplications is important. It's so important we have a rule for it:

BIDMAS

This tells us the correct order in which to do a combination of mathematical operations:

Brackets Indices Division Multiplication Addition Subtraction

PEMDAS is the American version of BIDMAS; Parentheses (Brackets) Exponents (Indices) Multiplication Division Addition Subtraction. Australian kids do not see PEMDAS very often but it is important to realise the P does NOT mean Powers (Indices) come first.

In case it wasn't clunky enough, BIDMAS is sometimes called BODMAS using 'Order' instead of 'Indices', but meaning exactly the same thing.

So what does BIDMAS mean? It tells us that when working out a series of operations, we firstly solve everything in brackets, then apply any indices (which are also called powers, exponents or orders). Then we do all division and multiplication going from left to right and then all addition and subtraction from left to right.

Look at how the placement of the brackets affects this statement:

$9 + 4 - 2 \times 6 = 9 + 4 - 12$ **(multiplication before addition and subtraction)** $= 1$ **(doing the addition and subtraction from left to right)**

$9 + (4 - 2) \times 6 = 9 + 2 \times 6$ **(doing the brackets first)** $= 9 + 12$ **(doing the multiplication next)** $= 21$

$(9 + 4) - 2 \times 6 = 13 - 2 \times 6$ **(doing the brackets first)** $= 13 - 12$ **(doing the multiplication next)** $= 1$

$[9 + (4 - 2)] \times 6$ **(an exciting case of 'double brackets' – we do the brackets before any other operations, and within the brackets we work from the inside out)** $= [9 + 2] \times 6 = 11 \times 6$ **(finishing off the brackets)** $= 66$

There were four completely different answers, depending on the place of the brackets, and using BIDMAS.

Can you see that:

$$10 \times 2 - 3^2 + 8 = 10 \times 2 - 9 + 8 \textbf{ (doing the indice } 3^2 \textbf{ first)}$$
$$= 20 - 9 + 8 \textbf{ (doing the multiplication next)}$$
$$= 19 \textbf{ (doing the addition and subtraction from}$$
$$\textbf{left to right)}$$

It's important to note that division and multiplication are considered 'equals' here. When we have division and multiplication next to each other, we do not do all division before all multiplication. It's the same, and occurs more often, with addition and subtraction.

So when working out $10 - 4 + 2$ we just operate left to right and get $10 - 4 + 2 = 6 + 2 = 8$.

We **DO NOT** do the addition first and get $10 - 4 + 2 = 10 - 6 = 4$.

Similarly $24 \div 2 \times 4 = 12 \times 4 = 48$ whereas $24 \div (2 \times 4) = 24 \div 8 = 3$.

So, the answer to our original internet meme?

$$4 - 4 \times 4 - 4 = 4 - 16 - 4 = -16$$

Make an equation out of the date

A teacher friend of mine uses this awesome little warm-up exercise in her maths class every day. They write out the date, either in full or abbreviated form. For example:

24/3/2021 or 24/3/21

and have to create valid equations using the digits of the date in the order they appear. The equals sign can go anywhere, you can throw in + − × and ÷, include brackets, use some numbers as powers, and you can skip zeroes if you want. Hey, if you're feeling brave you can even throw in a square root sign. Let me show you:

24/3/2021 would give us $2 \times 4 - 3 - 2 - 0 - 2 = 1$
or if you are feeling more adventurous
$2 \times 4 = 3^2 - 2 + 1$ or maybe
$2 \times \sqrt{4} - 3 - 2 + 2 = 1$

Similarly, 24/03/21 can create $2 \times 4 - (0 + 3)^2 = -1$

$(2 + 4) \div (3 \times 2) = 1$ or
$2 - 4 + 0 + 3 - 2 = -1$

Playing this game every day for a week or two is the perfect way to get your child (and you!) familiar with the very important rule that tells us 'the order of operations' ... BIDMAS!

NOT WHOLE
NUMBERS

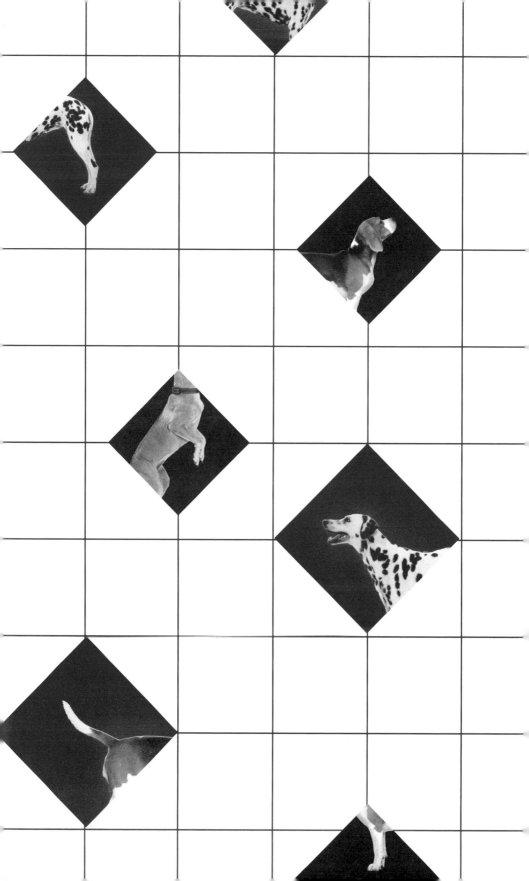

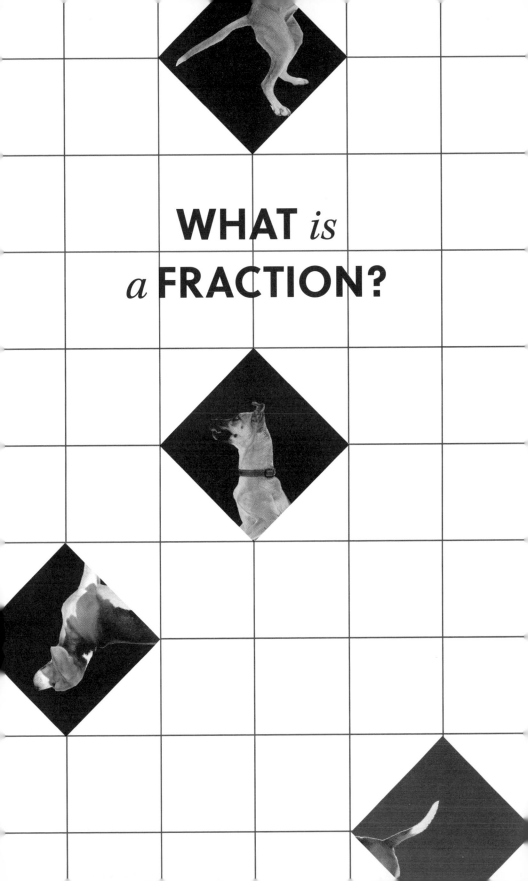

WHAT *is* *a* FRACTION?

It won't surprise you to know that we mathematicians have an official definition of a fraction. Trust me ... it's awesome. But at this early stage, as we help you dust off the cobwebs and introduce your child to the concept, let's not get bogged down in definitions.

After your child has learned to count, and mess around with whole numbers, the next type of numbers that they will encounter are fractions.

Fractions help us understand portions of numbers that are not whole numbers, and help us to describe things which are not whole things. Make sense? I find, like many other occasions in life, chocolate helps.

Here is a block of chocolate. Your child would probably quite happily gobble all of it down.

But if you and your child wanted to share the chocolate block, the fairest way to do so would be to split it in the middle.

This makes two equal pieces and you can have one each. Because you each get 'one' of the 'two' pieces, we write this as $\frac{1}{2}$ and call it 'one-half' or 'a half'.

If three of you wanted to share a chocolate bar, you could split it into three equal parts and take 'one-third' or $\frac{1}{3}$ each.

If one of your kids said 'nah, I'm fine', and you as the grown-up called dibs on two of the bits, you would take 'two-thirds' or $\frac{2}{3}$ of the chocolate bar and leave the other child $\frac{1}{3}$ (don't worry, I know full well it probably goes exactly the opposite way!).

And can you see that by breaking the chocolate bar into halves or thirds (or fifths, or anything else you'd like) and putting the pieces back together, that:

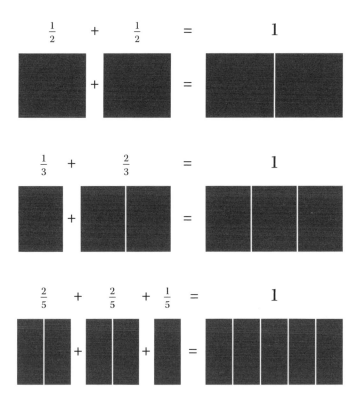

$$\frac{1}{2} \quad + \quad \frac{1}{2} \quad = \quad 1$$

$$\frac{1}{3} \quad + \quad \frac{2}{3} \quad = \quad 1$$

$$\frac{2}{5} \quad + \quad \frac{2}{5} \quad + \quad \frac{1}{5} \quad = \quad 1$$

If you'd like, draw lots of examples of chocolate bars broken into parts of equal size and write various equations showing how those pieces can make up a whole block.

We call the number on the bottom of a fraction the **'denominator'** (which always sounded to me a bit like 'dominator' and I thought was pretty cool). We call fractions with the same denominator 'like fractions'. In case you're wondering, the number on top of a fraction is called the **'numerator'**.

Now, we don't have to put back the entire chocolate bar. If I broke a chocolate bar into 5 equal pieces (fifths) and ate one piece of chocolate, can you see from rearranging what's left of the bar that:

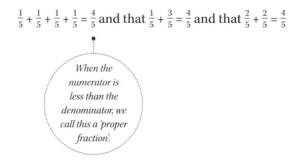

$$\frac{1}{5} + \frac{1}{5} + \frac{1}{5} + \frac{1}{5} = \frac{4}{5} \text{ and that } \frac{1}{5} + \frac{3}{5} = \frac{4}{5} \text{ and that } \frac{2}{5} + \frac{2}{5} = \frac{4}{5}$$

When the numerator is less than the denominator, we call this a 'proper fraction'.

Maybe do this with a few different chocolate bars and see if you can understand this very important rule about fractions

When we add like fractions, we keep the denominator the same and just add the numbers on top (the 'numerators').

What about when we subtract like fractions? Here is a block of chocolate left over from yesterday. It was divided into 5 equal pieces (fifths) and miraculously we still have 4 of those pieces left. So currently I have $\frac{4}{5}$ of a chocolate bar. If I ate one of these remaining pieces, I would now have three of those equal pieces (fifths) of the chocolate bar left. This shows us that:

Original bar $\qquad$ $\frac{4}{5}$ of the bar $\qquad$ $\frac{3}{5}$ are left
combining five 'fifths'

$$\frac{4}{5} - \frac{1}{5} = \frac{3}{5}$$

Draw a chocolate bar divided into the appropriate number of equal pieces and by starting with an incomplete bar and then crossing some of those pieces out, illustrate these equations:

$$\frac{6}{7} - \frac{4}{7} = \frac{2}{7}$$

$$\frac{5}{6} - \frac{1}{6} = \frac{4}{6}$$

$$\frac{7}{10} - \frac{4}{10} = \frac{3}{10}$$

$$\frac{3}{5} - \frac{3}{5} = \frac{0}{5} = 0$$

We can add and subtract like fractions all at once if we want to.

This diagram shows us that $\frac{2}{5} + \frac{2}{5} - \frac{1}{5} = \frac{3}{5}$

Original bar
combining five 'fifths'

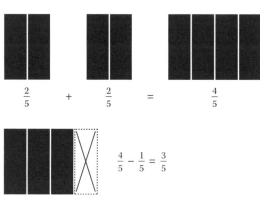

$$\frac{2}{5} \qquad + \qquad \frac{2}{5} \qquad = \qquad \frac{4}{5}$$

$$\frac{4}{5} - \frac{1}{5} = \frac{3}{5}$$

So $\frac{3}{7} + \frac{2}{7} - \frac{4}{7} =$ _____ ?

Again, if you draw the chocolate bar it will make things a bit easier to see. It will take longer, but trust me it will really sink in. Hopefully you got $\frac{1}{7}$ as the answer.

So far we've only dealt with adding or subtracting pieces up to and including one whole chocolate bar. But hey, who likes only one chocolate bar when you can have more?

Can you see that:

$\frac{3}{5} + \frac{3}{5} = \frac{6}{5}$ and that if we reassemble them like this ...

1 chocolate bar$\qquad\qquad$ $\frac{1}{5}$ of a bar

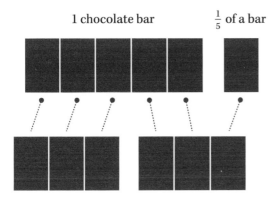

... can you see that $\frac{6}{5}$ is clearly $\frac{5}{5}$ with $\frac{1}{5}$ left over and that $\frac{5}{5}$ is 1?

So we have found that $\frac{3}{5} + \frac{3}{5} = \frac{6}{5} = 1\frac{1}{5}$

You want these terms to be interchangeable in your mind. You want to be able to see that $\frac{3}{5} + \frac{3}{5}$ and $\frac{6}{5}$ and $1\frac{1}{5}$ are exactly the same thing. We are not just memorising some rules here, we are trying to deeply understand how we add fractions together.

Convince yourself that:

$$\frac{2}{3} + \frac{2}{3} = 1\frac{1}{3}$$

$$\frac{5}{7} + \frac{6}{7} = 1\frac{4}{7}$$

$$\frac{4}{5} + \frac{4}{5} + \frac{3}{5} = 2\frac{1}{5}$$

Again, it might be best to draw the relevant chocolate bar to really understand what you are doing.

Each time, write the answer both as a fraction alone ('improper fraction') and as a whole number and a fraction (a 'mixed number').

Fractions where the numerator is greater than the denominator, like $\frac{8}{7}$, are called 'improper fractions'. Numbers written as whole numbers and a fraction, like $2\frac{1}{5}$, are called 'mixed numbers' or 'mixed fractions'.

Proper improper mixed

If we want to move easily between improper and mixed fractions it helps to notice the following:

Consider the mixed fraction $2\frac{3}{4}$

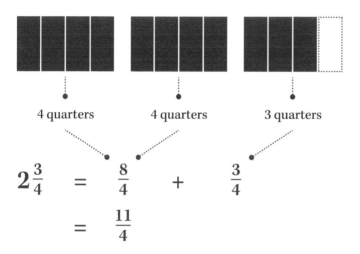

4 quarters   4 quarters   3 quarters

$$2\frac{3}{4} \quad = \quad \frac{8}{4} \quad + \quad \frac{3}{4}$$

$$= \quad \frac{11}{4}$$

The two whole chocolate bars provide 8 quarters because $2 \times 4 = 8$ and we still have $\frac{3}{4}$ of the third bar to add in.

$$\text{So, } 2\tfrac{3}{4} = \tfrac{8}{4} + \tfrac{3}{4} = \tfrac{11}{4}$$

Similarly:

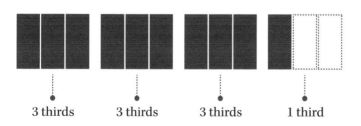

3 thirds   3 thirds   3 thirds   1 third

$$\text{We can see that } 3\tfrac{1}{3} = \tfrac{9}{3} + \tfrac{1}{3} = \tfrac{10}{3}$$

Draw some diagrams and convince yourself that
$2\frac{2}{3} = \frac{8}{3}$; $3\frac{1}{4} = \frac{13}{4}$; $4\frac{3}{5} = \frac{23}{5}$

Can you see this shortcut?

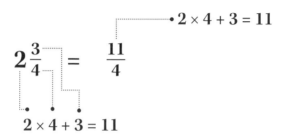

$$\bullet \, 2 \times 4 + 3 = 11$$

$$2\frac{3}{4} = \frac{11}{4}$$

$$2 \times 4 + 3 = 11$$

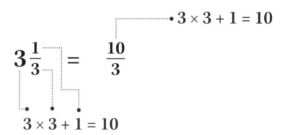

$$\bullet \, 3 \times 3 + 1 = 10$$

$$3\frac{1}{3} = \frac{10}{3}$$

$$3 \times 3 + 1 = 10$$

Try these examples. Turn these mixed numbers into improper fractions using the multiplication shortcut we just used.

$$3\frac{1}{4} = \frac{13}{4}; \quad 7\frac{2}{3} = \frac{23}{3}; \quad 8\frac{3}{5} = \frac{43}{5}$$

Now what about going back the other way? Can you turn these improper fractions into mixed numbers?

$$\frac{7}{4} = 1\frac{3}{4}; \quad \frac{9}{2} = 4\frac{1}{2}; \quad \frac{25}{3} = 8\frac{1}{3}$$

You probably worked these out in your head. When both numerator and denominator are comparatively small numbers, you can do it that way. For larger examples a bit of short division will help (if you don't know how to do these, have a quick look at page 71).

So to change the large improper fraction $\frac{254}{7}$ to a mixed number, we first divide 7 into 254.

$$7 \overline{)\,25^{4}4\,} \quad \begin{matrix} 3 \end{matrix}$$

7 into 25 goes 3 remainder 4

$$7 \overline{)\,25^{4}4\,} \quad \begin{matrix} 36\ r\,2 \end{matrix}$$

7 into 44 goes 6 remainder 2

So, $254 = 7 \times 36 + 2$

So, if we have $\frac{254}{7}$ we can think of that as $\frac{252}{7} + \frac{2}{7} = 36 + \frac{2}{7} = 36\frac{2}{7}$

$\frac{254}{7} = 36\frac{2}{7}$

Now, try changing these fractions from improper to mixed or mixed to improper:

$12\frac{2}{5}$; $\frac{37}{8}$; $6\frac{1}{9}$; $12\frac{3}{7}$; $\frac{47}{6}$

Answers: $12\frac{2}{5} = \frac{62}{5}$; $\frac{37}{8} = 4\frac{5}{8}$; $6\frac{1}{9} = \frac{55}{9}$; $12\frac{3}{7} = \frac{87}{7}$; $\frac{47}{6} = 7\frac{5}{6}$

Adding improper fractions

When adding mixed fractions, it's often easier to convert them to improper fractions, add them, then convert back:

$$3\frac{2}{5} + 4\frac{1}{5} = \frac{17}{5} + \frac{21}{5}$$
$$= \frac{38}{5}$$
$$= 7\frac{3}{5}$$

We change the answer from $\frac{38}{5}$ to $7\frac{3}{5}$ because if the question was written with mixed fractions, the answer should also be a mixed fraction unless specifically stated otherwise.

Similarly, when subtracting like, but improper, fractions:

$$5\frac{1}{5} - 3\frac{4}{5} = \frac{26}{5} - \frac{19}{5}$$
$$= \frac{7}{5}$$
$$= 1\frac{2}{5}$$

Note when adding mixed fractions with the same denominators, you can often save time by adding the whole numbers and adding the fractions then adding it all together. Huh, Adam? Check this out:

$$3\frac{2}{7} + 5\frac{4}{7} + 2\frac{3}{7} = 3 + 5 + 2 + \frac{2}{7} + \frac{4}{7} + \frac{3}{7}$$
$$= 10 + \frac{9}{7}$$
$$= 10 + 1\frac{2}{7}$$
$$= 11\frac{2}{7}$$

Adding different fractions

Okay, this is where things can get difficult for your child.

It's really important that your child follows what we do here and understands not just the pattern we follow when we add fractions, but what we are doing and why.

Let's start with an easy one. We know that $\frac{1}{2} + \frac{1}{2} = 1$ and that $\frac{1}{3} + \frac{1}{3} = \frac{2}{3}$.

But what about adding $\frac{1}{2} + \frac{1}{3}$?

Well first up, here is what you DON'T do. Many children panic when they see an example like:

I can't stress enough that this is a major pain point for a lot of kids who struggle with primary school mathematics.

$$\frac{1}{2} + \frac{1}{3}$$

They add the numerators and denominators and say:

$$\frac{1}{2} + \frac{1}{3} = \frac{2}{5} \quad \times$$

Can you see this is wrong? I mean, $\frac{2}{5}$ is less than a half and we can't add something to a half and end up with a lesser result, can we? If that was how we added fractions then $\frac{1}{2} + \frac{1}{2}$ would equal $\frac{2}{4}$, which is clearly not 1.

So, how do we add fractions with different denominators?

Look at these chocolate bars, with the half, one-third and two-thirds marks indicated. Placing the half and the third together, can you see that $\frac{1}{2} + \frac{1}{3}$ is equal to more than $\frac{2}{3}$ but less than 1? In fact, it looks to lie halfway between these two points.

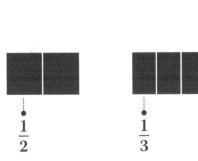

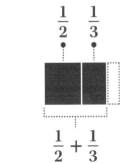

So the answer isn't some amount of halves or thirds, it must be something else. But what? As we saw earlier, it's easy to add similar fractions together. So what we are going to do is turn $\frac{1}{2}$ and $\frac{1}{3}$ into similar fractions and then add them.

Looking at these two chocolate bars that have been broken into six chunks can you see that $\frac{1}{2} = \frac{3}{6}$? And that $\frac{1}{3} = \frac{2}{6}$?

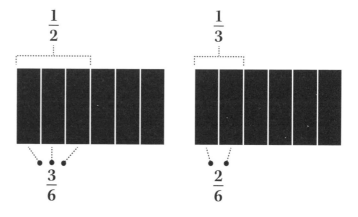

So adding the two fractions $\frac{1}{2} + \frac{1}{3}$ is the same as adding $\frac{3}{6} + \frac{2}{6}$.

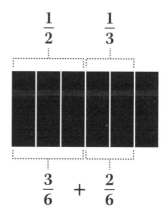

So $\frac{1}{2} + \frac{1}{3} = \frac{3}{6} + \frac{2}{6} = \frac{5}{6}$.

Let's try that again. Let's add $\frac{1}{3} + \frac{3}{4}$. Here's a hint: Divide your chocolate bar up into twelve chunks each. You should get $\frac{1}{3}$ + $\frac{3}{4} = \frac{13}{12}$ or $1\frac{1}{12}$.

'So Adam,' I hear you ask, 'how did you know to break the chocolate bar in 12 pieces?'

Well, dear reader, I was looking for a denominator that both $\frac{1}{3}$ and $\frac{3}{4}$ could be scaled up to. Can you see that: $\frac{1}{3} = \frac{2}{6} = \frac{3}{9} = \frac{4}{12}$ and $\frac{3}{4} = \frac{6}{8} = \frac{9}{12}$?

So $\frac{1}{3} + \frac{3}{4} = \frac{1 \times 4}{3 \times 4} + \frac{3 \times 3}{4 \times 3} = \frac{4}{12} + \frac{9}{12} = \frac{13}{12} = 1\frac{1}{12}$ and our common denominator 12 works precisely because $12 = 3 \times 4$.

Try these examples, and each time multiply the two denominators together to show you the new common denominator to use.

Show that $\frac{2}{3} + \frac{1}{5} = \frac{13}{15}$; $\frac{3}{4} - \frac{2}{3} = \frac{1}{12}$.

And if we are given three fractions, this example will show you how to obtain a common denominator:

$$\frac{1}{2} + \frac{2}{3} - \frac{3}{5} = \frac{1 \times 15}{2 \times 15} + \frac{2 \times 10}{3 \times 10} - \frac{3 \times 6}{5 \times 6}$$
$$= \frac{15}{30} + \frac{20}{30} - \frac{18}{30}$$
$$= \frac{17}{30}$$

Here, we have used $2 \times 3 \times 5 = 30$ as the common denominator where $30 = 2 \times 15 = 3 \times 10 = 5 \times 6$.

Comparing and ordering different fractions

Write the following fractions from smallest to largest:

$\frac{3}{2}; \frac{4}{3}; \frac{10}{7}$

Again, to compare these three fractions, it's best to obtain a common denominator. Let's use $2 \times 3 \times 7 = 42$.

$\frac{3}{2} = \frac{63}{42}; \frac{4}{3} = \frac{56}{42}; \frac{10}{7} = \frac{60}{42}$

So from smallest to largest we have $\frac{4}{3}, \frac{10}{7}, \frac{3}{2}$

Note we answer with the terms we were given, not the like fractions we created.

Find a fraction that lies between these two fractions and write the three fractions from smallest to largest:

$\frac{1}{2}$ and $\frac{3}{5}$

It is easy to compare fractions when we adjust them to have the same denominator.

So, calculating $2 \times 5 = 10$, we can rewrite the fractions as $\frac{1}{2} = \frac{5}{10}$ and $\frac{3}{5} = \frac{6}{10}$.

We can't squeeze another fraction with a denominator of 10 in between $\frac{5}{10}$ and $\frac{6}{10}$, but if we rewrite these fractions with larger denominators, we can make some room:

$\frac{5}{10} = \frac{10}{20}$ and $\frac{6}{10} = \frac{12}{20}$

$\frac{11}{20}$ lies in between these two fractions.

So $\frac{1}{2}, \frac{11}{20}, \frac{3}{5}$.

Simplifying fractions

To find a common denominator we used the fact that, for example, $\frac{1}{2} = \frac{2}{4} = \frac{3}{6} = \frac{4}{8}$ and so on.

We generated these 'equivalent fractions' by multiplying the numerator and denominator by the same amount. Well, we can also reduce a fraction to its simplest form by dividing the numerator and denominator by the same amount.

Can you see that $\frac{5}{10} = \frac{1}{2}$? It's probably obvious, but mathematically we are dividing the top and bottom of the fraction by 5.

Similarly, the fraction $\frac{15}{20}$ can be simplified as follows:

$$\frac{15}{20} = \frac{3 \times 5}{4 \times 5} = \frac{3 \times \cancel{5}}{4 \times \cancel{5}}$$

$$= \frac{3}{4}$$

Dividing numerator and denominator by 5, leaving $\frac{3}{4}$.

Similarly, to simplify $\frac{18}{27}$:

$$\frac{18}{27} = \frac{2 \times 9}{3 \times 9} = \frac{2 \times \cancel{9}}{3 \times \cancel{9}} = \frac{2}{3}$$

For larger numbers you might take a couple of steps to do the full simplification.

Simplify $\frac{72}{42}$:

$$\frac{72}{42} = \frac{36 \times 2}{21 \times 2} = \frac{36}{21} = \frac{12 \times 3}{7 \times 3} = \frac{12}{7}$$

Notice if we had seen that 6 was a common factor of the numerator and denominator we would have saved time and, most importantly, got the same answer:

$$\frac{72}{42} = \frac{12 \times 6}{7 \times 6} = \frac{12}{7}$$

It's really important that this long section on adding and subtracting fractions makes good sense for your child before we move on to the next bit. When children learn how to multiply fractions together, experience shows us they will then want to follow the same method when they add fractions. AND IT IS WRONG. Make sense? Probably not, but please trust me and thoroughly understand what's going on when we add and subtract fractions before proceeding.

Multiplying fractions

Look at these examples:

$$3 \times \frac{1}{5} = \frac{3}{5}$$

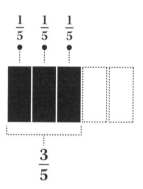

$$4 \times \frac{2}{5} = \frac{8}{5} = 1\frac{3}{5}$$

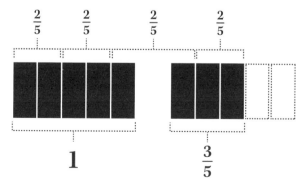

And $5 \times \frac{2}{3} = \frac{10}{3} = 3\frac{1}{3}$

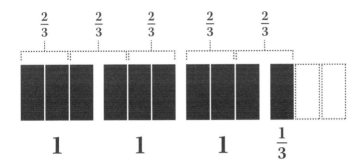

The rule we follow here is to write the whole number as a fraction with a denominator of 1 and multiply numerators and denominators.

E.g. $3 \times \frac{1}{5} = \frac{3}{1} \times \frac{1}{5} = \frac{3 \times 1}{1 \times 5} = \frac{3}{5}$; $4 \times \frac{2}{5} = \frac{4}{1} \times \frac{2}{5} = \frac{8}{5}$; $5 \times \frac{2}{3} = \frac{5}{1} \times \frac{2}{3} = \frac{10}{3}$.

Fractions multiplied by fractions

So what happens when we multiply a fraction not by a whole number, but by another fraction?

Hopefully you can see from these diagrams that $\frac{1}{2} \times \frac{1}{2} = \frac{1}{4}$ and $\frac{3}{4} \times \frac{1}{2} = \frac{3}{8}$.

$\frac{1}{2}$ **of** $\frac{1}{2} = \frac{1}{4}$ **of the chocolate** $\frac{3}{4}$ **of** $\frac{1}{2} = \frac{3}{8}$ **of the chocolate**

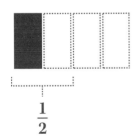   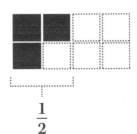

You can see we just follow the previous rule.

We multiply the numerators together and the denominators together to get our new fraction; for example $\frac{3}{4} \times \frac{1}{2} = \frac{3 \times 1}{4 \times 2} = \frac{3}{8}$.

Sometimes the answer needs to be simplified. For example:

$$\frac{2}{3} \times \frac{3}{4} = \frac{2 \times 3}{3 \times 4} = \frac{6}{12} = \frac{1}{2}$$

$$\frac{5}{18} \times \frac{3}{20} = \frac{15}{360} = \frac{5 \times 3}{120 \times 3} = \frac{5}{120} = \frac{5 \times 1}{5 \times 24} = \frac{1}{24}$$

Note with this example the numerators multiply together and the denominators multiply together and then we cancel out any common factors from the new fraction. We could actually simplify earlier in the process:

$$\frac{5}{18} \times \frac{3}{20} = \frac{5}{6 \times 3} \times \frac{3}{5 \times 4} = \frac{{}^{1}\cancel{5}}{6 \times \cancel{3}_{1}} \times \frac{\cancel{3}^{1}}{\cancel{5} \times 4_{1}} = \frac{1}{6} \times \frac{1}{4} = \frac{1}{24}$$

Sometimes it is easier to cancel out common factors earlier in the piece so the numerators and denominators don't get too large and hard to factorise.

Dividing by fractions

Dividing by fractions really freaks kids out, but if you think about what division means, it's not that hard to follow.

The equation $\frac{12}{4} = 3$ tells us exactly the same information as $12 = 3 \times 4$ or 'if you break 12 into chunks of 4, you will get 3 of them'.

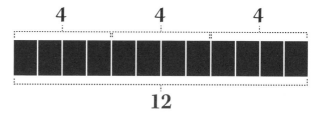

So let's consider $3 \div \frac{1}{2}$; like the prior example with 12 and 4, here we are asking 'if we break 3 into chunks of $\frac{1}{2}$, how many chunks of a $\frac{1}{2}$ will we get?'

As always, a diagram will help and, as always … I choose chocolate!

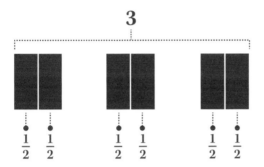

There are six $\frac{1}{2}$s in 3.

So, $3 \div \frac{1}{2} = 6$.

Draw some diagrams and convince yourself that $2 \div \frac{1}{3} = 6$, $5 \div \frac{1}{2} = 10$ and $3 \div \frac{1}{4} = 12$.

Now, what about more complicated fractions?

To calculate $4 \div \frac{2}{3}$ let's consider 4 chocolate bars, each broken into thirds:

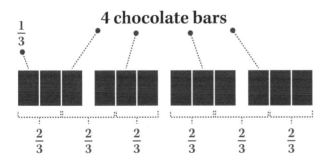

Can you see that there are 6 chunks of $\frac{2}{3}$ of a chocolate bar in our 4 chocolate bars?

$$\text{So, } 4 \div \frac{2}{3} = 6$$

Draw some chocolate bars and convince yourself that $4 \div \frac{2}{5} = 10$; $3 \div \frac{3}{4} = 4$; $5 \div \frac{5}{6} = 6$.

(Remember, to work out $4 \div \frac{2}{3}$ we broke our chocolate bar into $\frac{1}{3}$s – so each time, break the chocolate bar up into the number of pieces that matches the denominator of the fraction.)

Pay close attention to this example, where the chocolate bars don't split up perfectly evenly:

$$3 \div \frac{2}{3} =$$

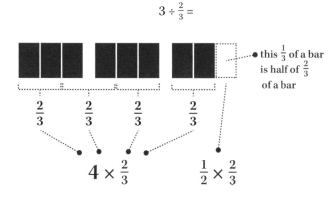

this $\frac{1}{3}$ of a bar is half of $\frac{2}{3}$ of a bar

Using 4 chunks of $\frac{2}{3}$ of a chocolate bar gets us as far as $2\frac{2}{3}$ or $\frac{8}{3}$ bars. We only need one more third. Can you see this is half of a $\frac{2}{3}$ chunk? So, we used 4 and a half chunks:

$$\text{So, } 3 \div \frac{2}{3} = 4\frac{1}{2} = \frac{9}{2}$$

Now this is the bit that confuses children and parents alike. There is a really cool shortcut we can do to avoid having to draw chocolate bars and break them up into chunks. Don't get me wrong, I LOVE chocolate, but this can take a fair bit of time.

Look at some of the answers you've got so far:

$$3 \div \tfrac{1}{2} = 6 \text{ and notice that } 3 \times \tfrac{2}{1} = 6$$

$$2 \div \tfrac{1}{3} = 6 \text{ and notice that } 2 \times \tfrac{3}{1} = 6$$

$$4 \div \tfrac{2}{3} = 6 \text{ and } 4 \times \tfrac{3}{2} = \tfrac{12}{2} = 6$$

$$5 \div \tfrac{5}{6} = 6 \text{ and } 5 \times \tfrac{6}{5} = \tfrac{30}{5} = 6$$

Even the nasty last example where the chunks didn't go evenly into the bars follows this same pattern:

$$3 \div \tfrac{2}{3} = 4\tfrac{1}{2} \text{ or } \tfrac{9}{2} \text{ and } 3 \times \tfrac{3}{2} = \tfrac{9}{2} = 4\tfrac{1}{2}$$

This pattern gives us the rule for when we divide by a fraction:

'When we divide a number by a fraction, flip over the fraction and multiply.'

Sarah has 5 cakes. How many people can she feed if she gives them a third of a cake each? **$5 \div \tfrac{1}{3} = 5 \times \tfrac{3}{1} = 15$**

What about fractions divided by fractions? We just do the same ... when we divide a number by a fraction, invert the fraction and multiply.

Consider $\tfrac{1}{3} \div \tfrac{1}{6}$

The rule of 'invert and multiply' tells us $\tfrac{1}{3} \div \tfrac{1}{6} = \tfrac{1}{3} \times \tfrac{6}{1} = 2.$

And what does that mean?

Here is a chocolate bar split into thirds. But if we divide one third into sixths, you should be able to see that we do get two sixths.

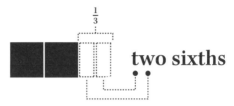

So yes, $\frac{1}{3} \div \frac{1}{6} = 2$.

And if we get a question involving mixed numbers, we just make them improper fractions and go from there.

$$3\frac{3}{5} \div 2\frac{1}{2} = \frac{18}{5} \div \frac{5}{2} = \frac{18}{5} \times \frac{2}{5} = \frac{36}{25} = 1\frac{11}{25}$$

Mauro walks $2\frac{1}{3}$ laps of the oval in $15\frac{3}{4}$ minutes. How long does it take him to complete a lap to the nearest second?

$$15\frac{3}{4} \div 2\frac{1}{3} = \frac{63}{4} \div \frac{7}{3} = \frac{63}{4} \times \frac{3}{7} = \frac{27}{4} = 6\frac{3}{4} \text{ minutes} = 6 \text{ minutes}$$
$$45 \text{ seconds}$$

Fractions, percentages and decimals

We explain percentages and decimals in the next two chapters of the book – you might want to check them quickly and come back.

These tables contain some handy and commonly used fractions, percentages and decimals.

A great way to practise these is to write them out from scratch and compare them to the answers here. Your child should know all of these values.

Fraction	Decimal	Percentage
$\frac{1}{2}$	0.5	50
$\frac{1}{4}$	0.25	25
$\frac{3}{4}$	0.75	75
$\frac{1}{5}$	0.2	20
$\frac{2}{5}$	0.4	40
$\frac{3}{5}$	0.6	60
$\frac{4}{5}$	0.8	80

Fraction	Decimal	Percentage
$\frac{1}{3}$	$0.\dot{3}$	$33.\dot{3}$ or $33\frac{1}{3}$
$\frac{2}{3}$	$0.\dot{6}$	$66.\dot{6}$ or $66\frac{2}{3}$
$\frac{1}{9}$	$0.\dot{1}$	$11.\dot{1}$ or $11\frac{1}{9}$
$\frac{2}{9}$	$0.\dot{2}$	$22.\dot{2}$ or $22\frac{2}{9}$
$\frac{3}{9} = \frac{1}{3}$	$0.\dot{3}$	$33.\dot{3}$ or $33\frac{1}{3}$
$\frac{4}{9}$	$0.\dot{4}$	$44.\dot{4}$ or $44\frac{4}{9}$
$\frac{5}{9}$	$0.\dot{5}$	$55.\dot{5}$ or $55\frac{5}{9}$
$\frac{6}{9} = \frac{2}{3}$	$0.\dot{6}$	$66.\dot{6}$ or $66\frac{2}{3}$
$\frac{7}{9}$	$0.\dot{7}$	$77.\dot{7}$ or $77\frac{7}{9}$
$\frac{8}{9}$	$0.\dot{8}$	$88.\dot{8}$ or $88\frac{8}{9}$

Perhaps the toughest fractions that do come up occasionally are the $\frac{1}{8}$ s.

Here's a good way to understand your way around the eighths.

It should be clear that $\frac{1}{2}$ = 0.5 = 50%. These three quantities are all equal. They are interchangeable. To eat

$\frac{1}{2}$ of a cake is the same as consuming 50%. And while you would very rarely say it, you could just as accurately say, 'Wow, I just scoffed down 0.5 of that cake.'

If we split a half in half, we get a quarter. And we could do the same to the other quantities here so we get $\frac{1}{4}$ = 0.25 = 25%. Again, these three quantities are all the same. And multiplying these by 3 gives us $\frac{3}{4}$ = 0.75 = 75%.

Well, to get the $\frac{1}{8}$s we just do the same, chop the quarters in half again:

$$\frac{1}{8} = 0.125 = 12.5\% \text{ or } 12\frac{1}{2}\%$$

These tend to scare students, but they come easily from the quarters.

So we fill out this final table by starting with $\frac{1}{8}$ = 0.125 = $12\frac{1}{2}$% and multiplying up from there.

Fraction	Decimal	Percentage
$\frac{1}{8}$	0.125	12.5 or $12\frac{1}{2}$
$\frac{2}{8} = \frac{1}{4}$	0.25	25
$\frac{3}{8}$	0.375	37.5
$\frac{4}{8} = \frac{1}{2}$	0.5	50
$\frac{5}{8}$	0.625	62.5
$\frac{6}{8} = \frac{3}{4}$	0.75	75
$\frac{7}{8}$	0.875	87.5
$\frac{8}{8} = 1$	1	100

Can I stress, this will stay with your child much longer if they genuinely understand what we are doing and why. If they just commit patterns to memory without understanding what they are doing, these concepts won't stick and may plague them for years.

And that, dear reader, covers just about everything you need to know in the wonderful world of (primary school) fractions.

Extension!

Frac-tastic

Have a look at this fraction sum:

$$\frac{24}{138} + \frac{57}{69} = \frac{24}{138} + \frac{57 \times 2}{69 \times 2} = \frac{24}{138} + \frac{114}{138} = \frac{138}{138} = 1$$

and notice that the two fractions we started with used the digits 1 to 9 exactly once each. Wow! Pretty cool, hey?

Notice how finding the common denominator of 138 was not that hard to do because 69 is a factor of 138.

Now convince yourself that $\frac{27}{189} + \frac{54}{63} = 1$ (again, 63 is a factor of 189, so the common denominator of 189 is not hard to obtain).

Now try and complete these fraction sums. They each add up to exactly 1, using the digits 1 to 9 once and once only. In each case the smaller denominator is a factor of the larger one; or the fractions simplify significantly e.g. $\frac{27}{189} = \frac{1}{7}$.

$$\frac{34}{158} + \frac{??}{79} \; ; \; \frac{?2}{6?1} + \frac{?7}{93} \; ; \; \frac{58}{174} + \frac{??}{39} \; ; \; \frac{??}{1?4} + \frac{62}{93} \; ;$$

$$\frac{??}{138} + \frac{??}{54} \; ; \; \frac{?6?}{?12} + \frac{?}{57}$$

Answers: $\frac{34}{158} + \frac{62}{79} \; ; \; \frac{42}{651} + \frac{87}{93} \; ; \; \frac{58}{174} + \frac{26}{39} \; ; \; \frac{58}{174} + \frac{62}{93} \; ; \; \frac{69}{138} + \frac{27}{54} \; ; \; \frac{864}{912} + \frac{3}{57}$

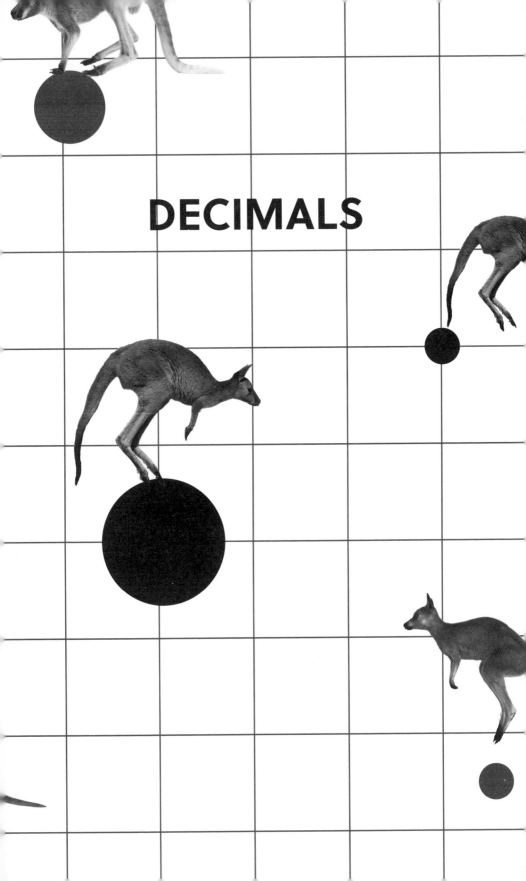

DECIMALS

We use decimals all the time:

'I'm down to 87.6 kg.'

'Usain Bolt smashed the world record running 100 metres in 9.58 seconds.'

'The Aussie dollar is trading at 65.86 US cents.'

'My Uber driver is rated 4.7 stars.'

But we get a little bit scared when they pop up in mathematics. They are not that bad. Let's check them out.

Drop the base (10)

Our counting system is built around the number 10. It's probably because that's the number of fingers we have. There are systems today (the 12 hours on a clock) and throughout history (the Babylonians counting by 60s) that have been different but, by and large, numerically we are a society based in 10s.

The number 3058 literally means:

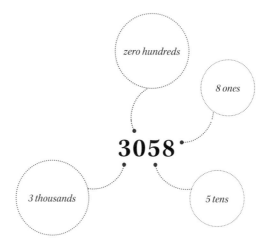

As numbers get bigger, we move to a new place column which is a new '**power**' of 10.

Well, we also use powers of 10 to describe numbers, or parts of numbers that lie between 0 and 1.

So 34.15 represents:

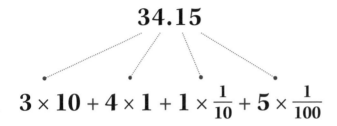

$$3 \times 10 + 4 \times 1 + 1 \times \frac{1}{10} + 5 \times \frac{1}{100}$$

Similarly, $\mathbf{3.01} = 3 + 0 \times \frac{1}{10} + 1 \times \frac{1}{100} = 3 + \frac{1}{100}$ **and**

$$0.37 = \frac{3}{10} + \frac{7}{100}$$

Notice this, too: $\frac{3}{10} = \frac{30}{100}$

So 0.37 can also be written as $\frac{3}{10} + \frac{7}{100} = \frac{30}{100} + \frac{7}{100} = \frac{37}{100}$

Understanding this makes it easy to move between decimals, fractions and percentages.

$$0.37 = \frac{37}{100} = 37\%$$

$$0.75 = \frac{75}{100} = \frac{3}{4} = 75\%$$

$$0.06 = \frac{6}{100} = 6\%$$

And can you see that $0.015 = \frac{1}{100} + \frac{5}{1000} = \frac{15}{1000} = \frac{1.5}{100} = 1.5\%$?

Changing fractions to decimals

When the denominator (the number on the bottom of the fraction) is 10 or a power of 10, it is easy to change a fraction into a decimal.

$\frac{37}{100} = 0.37$ as we saw before. Or,

$\frac{7}{10} = 0.7; \quad \frac{13}{10} = 1.3; \quad \frac{7013}{100} = 70.13$

If the denominator is not a power of 10, the fraction might easily be changed to an equivalent fraction with such a denominator.

$\frac{37}{50} \times \frac{2}{2} = \frac{74}{100} = 0.74$

$\frac{7}{20} \times \frac{5}{5} = \frac{35}{100} = 0.35$

$\frac{7}{5} \times \frac{2}{2} = \frac{14}{10} = 1.4$

$\frac{1}{4} \times \frac{25}{25} = \frac{25}{100} = 0.25$

But with practice, some fractions will just become obvious.

$\frac{1}{5} = 0.2$, which you should be able to see because 0.2×5 clearly equals 1.

So, $\frac{2}{5} = 2 \times 0.2 = 0.4$; $\frac{3}{5} = 0.6$ and $\frac{4}{5} = 0.8$. Once we get above 1, $\frac{6}{5} = 1 + \frac{1}{5} = 1.2$; $\frac{7}{5} = 1.4$; $\frac{8}{5} = 1.6$ and so on.

$\frac{1}{4} = 0.25$ as we calculated above, but after a while you should be able to see instantly that $0.25 \times 4 = 1$, so 0.25 is obviously $\frac{1}{4}$.

So, $\frac{3}{4} = 3 \times 0.25 = 0.75$; $\frac{5}{4} = 1.25$; $\frac{7}{4} = 1.75$ and away we go!

Arrange these quantities from smallest to largest:

$$0.7, 65\%, \frac{3}{4}$$

To compare them it helps to make them all the same sort of quantity. Let's go for decimals (we could just as well do percentages or fractions):

$0.7 = 0.7;\ \ 65\% = 0.65;\ \ \frac{3}{4} = 0.75$

So, arranged from smallest to largest we get: 0.65, 0.7, 0.75 or 65%, 0.7, $\frac{3}{4}$.

Adding decimals together

You should be able to see that $0.2 + 0.5 = \frac{2}{10} + \frac{5}{10} = \frac{7}{10} = 0.7$

that $0.4 + 0.9 = \frac{4}{10} + \frac{9}{10} = \frac{13}{10} = 1.3$

and that $1.3 + 0.5 + 0.8 = \frac{13}{10} + \frac{5}{10} + \frac{8}{10} = \frac{26}{10} = 2.6$.

But we can also do these types of sums using our addition algorithm from page 32, for example:

$$
\begin{array}{r}
0.\overset{\bullet}{2}\ + \\
0.5 \\
\hline
0.7
\end{array}
\qquad
\begin{array}{r}
{}^{1}\ \bullet \\
0.4\ + \\
0.9 \\
\hline
1.3
\end{array}
$$

Line up the decimal points and add accordingly.

Just carry the one into the next column.

Now for some harder ones, but don't panic!

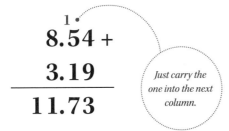

$$
\begin{array}{r}
{}^{1}\ \bullet \\
8.54\ + \\
3.19 \\
\hline
11.73
\end{array}
$$

Just carry the one into the next column.

$$5.041\ +$$
$$3.4$$
$$6.82$$
$$\overline{15.261}$$

$$5.041\ +$$
$$3.400\ \cdot$$
$$6.820$$
$$\overline{15.261}$$

Adding zeroes helps us line up the digits and doesn't change anything. Here, 3.400 is the same as 3.4.

Subtracting decimals

You probably won't be surprised to learn that when we subtract decimals, we use the good old subtraction algorithm. Again, don't forget to line up the decimal places:

$0.8 - 0.3 = \frac{8}{10} - \frac{3}{10} = \frac{5}{10} = 0.5$ and

$$0.8\ -$$
$$0.3$$
$$\overline{0.5}$$

Line up the decimal points and subtract accordingly.

$$1.43 - 0.85 = \frac{143}{100} - \frac{85}{100} = \frac{58}{100} = 0.58$$

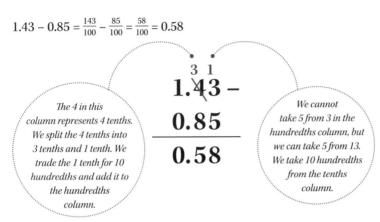

The 4 in this column represents 4 tenths. We split the 4 tenths into 3 tenths and 1 tenth. We trade the 1 tenth for 10 hundredths and add it to the hundredths column.

$$\begin{array}{r} \overset{3\;\;1}{1.4\!\!\!\diagup\!\!3} - \\ 0.85 \\ \hline 0.58 \end{array}$$

We cannot take 5 from 3 in the hundredths column, but we can take 5 from 13. We take 10 hundredths from the tenths column.

Leah bought lunch for herself, Tai and Indi. The meals cost $11.85, $9.65 and $6 respectively. How much did the meals cost? Leah tipped the waitress 10%. How much was the tip? She paid with a $50 note. How much change did she get?

$$\begin{array}{r} \$11.85 + \\ 9.65 \\ 6.00 \\ \hline \$27.50 \end{array}$$

The meals cost $27.50. The tip was 10% (or $\frac{1}{10}$) of that, which is $2.75. So Leah paid $27.50 + $2.75 = $30.25. Her change would be:

$$\begin{array}{r} \$50.00 - \\ 30.25 \\ \hline \$19.75 \end{array}$$

Multiplying decimals

Let's start with some easy examples.

Let's multiply 0.3 by 10:

$0.3 \times 10 = \frac{3}{10} \times 10 = 3$. We can also see this with our old friend, the chocolate bar. If we chop the bar into 10 pieces and add up ten 3-piece chunks, we get exactly 3 chocolate bars. I've labelled the chunks 1 to 10.

Each of these chunks is $\frac{3}{10}$ of a bar

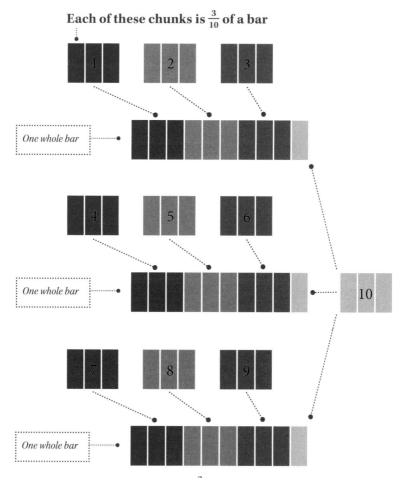

Ten chunks, each $0.3 = \frac{3}{10}$ of a bar, add up to exactly 3 bars.

What about 0.65 × 10?

$$0.65 \times 10 = \frac{65}{100} \times 10 = \frac{650}{100} = \frac{65}{10} = 6.5$$

Let's keep looking:

$$3.072 \times 10 = \frac{3072}{1000} \times 10 = \frac{3072}{100} = 30.72$$

Can you see that multiplying a decimal by 10 is the same as moving the decimal point one place to the right and otherwise the digits remain unchanged? Each digit increases in value 10 times, so it looks like the decimal point has moved.

0.6 × 10

$$\times\ 10$$

0.6.000

6.000

so 0.6 × 10 = 6

$$
\begin{array}{r}
0.65 \\
\times \quad 10 \\
\hline
\end{array}
$$

= 0.6.5 = 6.5

$$
\begin{array}{r}
3.072 \\
\times \quad 10 \\
\hline
\end{array}
$$

= 3.0.72 = 30.72

Guess what happens if we multiply a decimal by 100? Well, that's the same as multiplying by 10 and then by 10 again, so you'd expect the decimal point to move **TWO** decimal places to the right. As it turns out, that's exactly what happens.

Consider 0.3×100.

To see how the decimal place moves we will write this as:

$$\mathbf{0.3000 \times 100}$$

$$\times\, \mathbf{100}$$

Is it clear that 0.3000 = 0.3? The extra zeroes make no difference to the value of 0.3 but help us to see what is happening.

$$= \mathbf{0.30\!:\!00}$$

$$= \mathbf{30.0 = 30}$$

0.65×100

$= \frac{65}{100} \times 100 = 65$

$0.65. \times 100 = 65$

$3.072 \times 100 =$

$\frac{3072}{1000} \times 100 = \frac{3072}{10}$

$= 307.2$

$3.07.2 \times 100 = 307.2$

With this last example you should be able to see that 3.072 is 'just a bit more than 3' so multiplying by 100 should give us something 'just a bit more than 300' ... and it does. It helps to have this sense of size so if you accidentally move the decimal point too far, or not far enough, you will 'feel' that something is wrong.

If you got the answer:

$$\times\quad \mathbf{3.072. \times 100 = 3072}$$

Oops – moved the decimal point 3 places not 2!!!

or

$$\times\quad \mathbf{3.0.72 \times 100 = 30.72}$$

you should immediately realise 'hold on a second'; that can't be right'.

Multiplying a decimal by 1000

You shouldn't be surprised that the decimal point moves three places to the right.

So, $0.3 \times 1000 =$ **0.30000 × 1000 ... move the decimal point three places right** = **300.00** = 300.

$$0.65 \times 1000 = 650; \; 3.072 \times 1000 = 3072$$

Convert these quantities to the new units:

2.75 kilograms into grams; there are 1000 grams in a kilogram, so 2.75 kg = 2.75 × 1000 g = 2750 g

3.8 metres to centimetres; there are 100 centimetres in a metre, so 3.8 m = 3.8 × 100 cm = 380 cm

Dividing by 10, 100, 1000

Watch what happens to the decimal place when we divide by 10, 100 and 1000:

$$37 \div 10 = \tfrac{37}{10} = 3.7.0 = 3.7$$

$$8 \div 100 = \tfrac{8}{100} = 0.08.0 = 0.08$$

Writing 8 as 0008.00 you can see that as the decimal point moves two places to the left:

00.08.00 becomes 0.08

So dividing 8 by 100 moves the decimal point two spots to the left.

We don't normally write these extra zeroes in front and behind a number, but putting them in doesn't change anything and helps keep track of how far a decimal point has moved.

After a while you won't need to write the extra zeroes, and your thinking should be something along the lines of this diagram:

$$\vdots\ 8 \rightarrow 0 \vdots 0\,8$$
$$= 0.08$$

Now look at the case of division by 1000:

$$27 \div 1000 = \frac{27}{1000} = 0.027$$

$$0\vdots 0\,2\,7$$

After a bit of practice you don't need to do the middle step on these multiplication and division problems. You can just move the decimal point the required number of places.

Multiplying decimals by whole numbers other than 10

To multiply a decimal number by a whole number we use our old mate the multiplication algorithm:

$0.23 - \frac{1}{100} \times 23$

So, $0.23 \times 5 = \frac{1}{100} \times 23 \times 5$

$\qquad = \frac{1}{100} \times 115$

$\qquad = 1.15$

That's why the number of decimal places in the equation and the answer match up.

$$\begin{array}{r} 0.23 \times \\ 5 \\ \hline 1.15 \end{array}$$

There are two decimal places in the number being multiplied, so the answer must contain two decimal places.

$$4.023 \times$$
$$53$$
$$\overline{213.219}$$

$4023 \times 53 = 213219$
But $4.023 = \frac{1}{1000} \times 4023$
So, again, the answer has
3 decimal points.

Again, there are three decimal places in the product, so there are three in the answer.

Dividing a decimal by a whole number other than 10, 100, 1000

When we used our division algorithm back in the Multplication and Division chapter we saw that sometimes the answer comes out evenly and leaves no remainder. Here's an example in all its step-by-step glory:

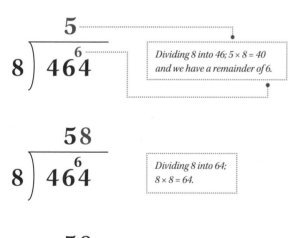

Dividing 8 into 46; 5 × 8 = 40 and we have a remainder of 6.

Dividing 8 into 64; 8 × 8 = 64.

So 464 ÷ 8 = 58.

But if the division does not give us a whole number as an answer, we can write a remainder.

For example, 467 ÷ 8 = 58 remainder 3:

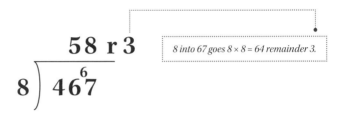

$$58\,r\,3$$
$$8\,)\,\overline{46^{6}7}$$

8 into 67 goes 8 × 8 = 64 remainder 3.

Another way to do this is to write the 467 with a decimal point and some zeroes, and get a decimal as our answer instead of a remainder.

$$58.375$$
$$8\,)\,\overline{46^{6}7.^{3}0^{6}0^{4}0}$$

467 ÷ 8 = 58.375

Solve 72.4 ÷ 5:

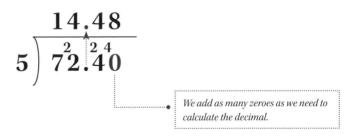

$$14.48$$
$$5\,)\,\overline{7^{2}2.^{2}4^{4}0}$$

We add as many zeroes as we need to calculate the decimal.

Sometimes the answer does not stop, or 'terminate'. Two examples every student needs to know are:

$$0.333\ldots$$
$$3\overline{)1.000\ldots}$$

$$0.111\ldots$$
$$9\overline{)1.000\ldots}$$

To signify that the 3s and 1s go on forever, here we write:

$$0.\dot{3} \text{ and } 0.\dot{1}$$

These two results, that:

$$\frac{1}{3} = 0.333\ldots = 0.\dot{3}$$

and

$$\frac{1}{9} = 0.111\ldots = 0.\dot{1}$$

are crucial results that every student has to know. It's best to do the short division exercise as we see it here a few times so the result really sinks in and isn't just committed to memory.

Extension!

Some sweeter repeaters

Use the division algorithm to show that:

$\frac{1}{7} = 0.142857\ 142857...$

$\frac{1}{11} = 0.090909...$

$\frac{1}{41} = 0.02439\ 02439...$

> *Note: when a string of numbers repeats, we use a line above the numbers.*

So $0.\overline{09} = 0.090909...$

$$\frac{1}{7} = 0.\overline{142857142857142857...}$$
$$= 0.\overline{142857}$$

and so on ...

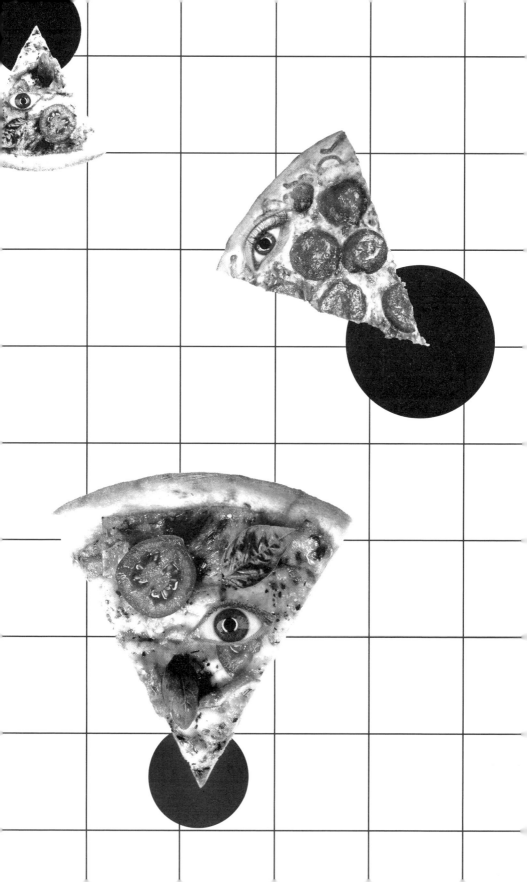

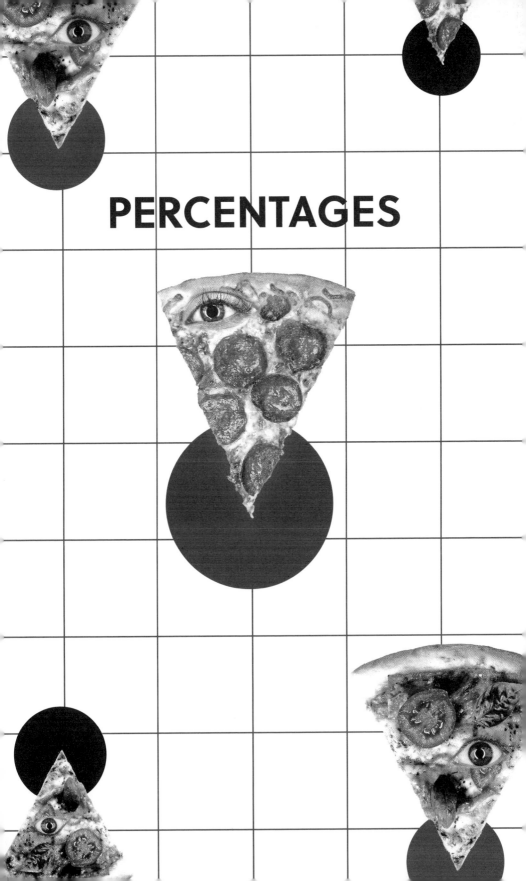

PERCENTAGES

To me, percentages are a bit of a weird one. Most people readily use percentages in their daily lives.

'85% in Maths – I'm so proud of you.'

'The boys gave 110% today.'

'I got it for 40% off ... BARGAIN!'

But as soon as the dreaded % sign sneaks into maths homework, some parents run for the hills.

Well, as you'll read many times in this book, it's really not that bad if you take it nice and slowly.

The most important thing with percentages is **to remember what the term 'per cent' means**.

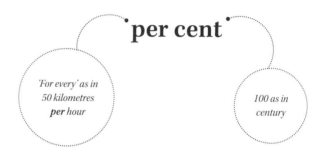

'per cent'

*'For every' as in
50 kilometres
per hour*

*100 as in
century*

'Per cent' means 'for every hundred'.

So '85% in Maths' means that for every 100 marks available, you got 85.

So, can you see that 85% is the same as the fraction $\frac{85}{100}$?

And from page 142 we can simplify this fraction by cancelling a factor of 5 top and bottom of the fraction to get:

$$85\% = \frac{85}{100} \quad \frac{17 \times \cancel{5}}{20 \times \cancel{5}} = \frac{17}{20}$$

So to **turn percentages into fractions** we just write the percentage as a fraction with a denominator (bottom number) of 100 and simplify if we can.

So, check that $50\% = \frac{50}{100} = \frac{1}{2}$

$80\% = \frac{80}{100} = \frac{4}{5}$

$37\% = \frac{37}{100}$ which can't be simplified.

And can you see that:

$$25\% = \frac{1}{4}; \ 60\% = \frac{3}{5}; \ 70\% = \frac{7}{10}; \ 12\% = \frac{3}{25}; \ 250\% = \frac{5}{2} = 2\frac{1}{2};$$
$$100\% = 1; \ 400\% = 4$$

To **turn fractions into percentages** we just multiply the fraction by 100% (which is the same as multiplying it by 1).

$$\text{So,} \ \frac{1}{5} = \frac{1}{5} \times 100\% = \frac{100\%}{5} = 20\%; \ \frac{3}{4} = \frac{3}{4} \times 100\% = \frac{300\%}{4} = 75\%;$$
$$\frac{1}{8} = \frac{1}{8} \times 100\% = \frac{100\%}{8} = 12.5\%$$

Can you do the middle step of multiplying by 100% and see that:

$$\frac{3}{10} = 30\%; \ \frac{4}{5} = 80\%; \ \frac{11}{20} = 55\%; \ \frac{3}{8} = 37.5\%; \ 3\frac{1}{2} = \frac{7}{2} = 350\%;$$
$$\text{and} \ \frac{2}{3} = 66.\dot{6}\% = 66\frac{2}{3}\%$$

There are 200 children at Olivia's school. Every day 50% arrive at the school by bus, 20% are driven by their parents, and the rest walk to school. How many children walk to school?

50% + 20% = 70%. So 70% of the students either arrive by bus or their parents drive them.

This leaves 100% – 70% = 30% who walk to school.

30% of 200 students is 30% × 200 = $\frac{30}{100}$ × 200.

$$\frac{30}{100} \times 200 = \frac{30}{1\cancel{00}} \times 2\cancel{00}$$

= 30 × 2 = 60 students walk to school each day.

Leah and her friend went out to lunch and the bill came to $80. The service was so good Leah gave a 15% tip. How much did she pay?

The tip was 15% of $80:

15% × $80 = $\frac{15}{10\cancel{0}}$ × 8$\cancel{0}$ = $\frac{15}{10}$ × 8 = $\frac{120}{10}$ = $12

So, Leah paid $80 + $12 = $92.

A $500 games console is reduced by 40%. How much does it now cost?

Reduction = 40% of $500 = $\frac{40}{100}$ × 500 = $\frac{40}{1\cancel{00}}$ × 5$\cancel{00}$
= $\frac{40}{1}$ × 5 = $200

So, the discounted price is $500 – $200 – $300.

Or we could do it this way:

If the price is reduced 40% you will only pay 60% of the original price.

60% × $500 = $\frac{60}{1\cancel{00}}$ × 5$\cancel{00}$ = 60 × 5 = $300

Say instead the $500 was reduced by 20% and one week later by another 20%. Does it cost the same as it did after the 40% reduction above?

Work through this and see that the first reduction is 20% of $500 = $100 taking the price to $400. The second reduction is 20% of $400 = $80 taking the price to $320.

So no, **two reductions of 20% is not the same as a straight discount of 40%.**

If we know ten per cent of something, or if it is easy to calculate ten percent, we can do some mental gymnastics with percentages to find other amounts.

A new pair of jeans costs $140, but has been reduced by 15%. What is the new price?
10% of 140 is 14
So 5% is 7
And 15% is 14 + 7 = 21
So the discounted price is $140 – $21 = $119

If the cost of a mobile phone bill goes up by 3% at the end of a promotion and the promotion price was $80, what is the new price?
10% of 80 is 8
1% of 80 is 0.8
3% of 80 is 3 × 0.8 = 2.4
The new price is $80 + $2.40 = $82.40

As I've said elsewhere in this book, it often helps to check the answer 'feels right'. If you can see that 3% of $100 is $3, then 3% of $80 = $2.40 should 'feel right'. So, 3% of $80 = $24 or 3% of $80 = 24 cents should 'feel wrong'. **This is a very powerful intuition for a student to have. Work on it!**

Turning a percentage into a decimal

By the end of primary school your child will have encountered percentages, fractions, whole numbers and decimals. Not only do they need to understand each of these, they need to be able to move seamlessly between them all.

We have already swapped between percentages and fractions. Now let's practise moving between percentages and decimals.

We know that $37\% = \frac{37}{100}$

But $\frac{37}{100} = 0.37$

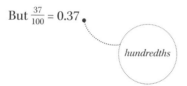

hundredths

Don't forget how decimals work (if you're thinking 'I did forget' don't worry, there's a whole chapter on decimals just waiting for you!). The second place after the decimal point represents hundredths.

Examine the following examples and make sure they make sense:

$9\% = \frac{9}{100} = 0.09$; $20\% = \frac{20}{100} = 0.20 = 0.2$; $120\% = \frac{120}{100} = \frac{12}{10} = 1.2$.

Doing the middle step by yourself, check that:

$$14\% = \underline{\hspace{2cm}} = 0.14$$
$$4\% = \underline{\hspace{2cm}} = 0.04$$
$$40\% = \underline{\hspace{2cm}} = 0.4$$
$$400\% = \underline{\hspace{2cm}} = 4$$
$$440\% = \underline{\hspace{2cm}} = 4.4$$

To go the other way, to turn a decimal into a percentage, here is a handy tip:

Write the decimal as a fraction with a denominator of 100. Then it is easy to read off the percentage.

$0.65 = \frac{65}{100} = 65\%$; $0.06 = \frac{6}{100} = 6\%$; $14.2 = \frac{142}{10} = \frac{1420}{100} = 1420\%$;

$0.317 = \frac{317}{1000} = \frac{31.7}{100} = 31.7\%$.

It's easy when you start out to get these answers wrong by a factor of 10. So you should always be checking if your answer 'feels right'. But Adam, maths isn't about 'the feels'. Yes, it can be. This is what I mean:

Look at the decimals 0.6, 0.06 and 6.6. Convince yourself that as fractions they are 60%, 6% and 660% respectively. This should 'feel right'. In the case of 0.6, it is just over a half (0.5) and 60% is just over 50%, which is also a half. If you had made a mistake and calculated that 0.6 = 6% or 600%, that should not 'feel right'. Similarly, 0.06 is less than 0.1 which is $\frac{1}{10}$ or 10%. So 0.06 = 6% should feel right. Finally, because 100% = 1, then 6.6 = 660% should look pretty good as an answer.

After a while you should realise that multiplying or dividing by 100 is the same as moving the decimal place to the right or to the left by two places. We saw this in our chapter on decimals. As such, going from decimals to percentages and back becomes reasonably easy to do, and the amounts 42% and 0.42 should obviously be the same quantities.

It hopefully also helps you understand the important recurring decimals we've already met.

$$\frac{1}{3} = 0.333\ldots = 0.\dot{3} = 33.\dot{3}\% = 33\frac{1}{3}\%$$

$$\frac{2}{3} = 0.666\ldots = 0.\dot{6} = 66.\dot{6}\% = 66\frac{2}{3}\%$$

ADVENTURES
IN 2D AND 3D

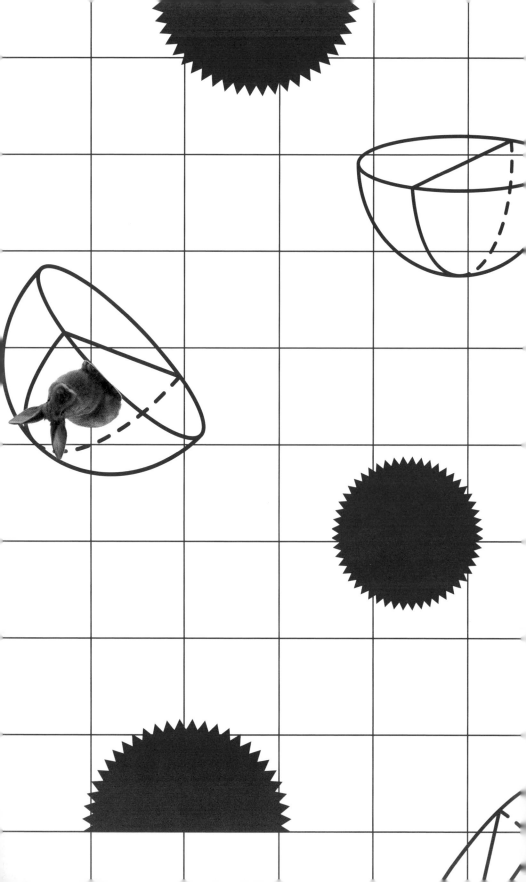

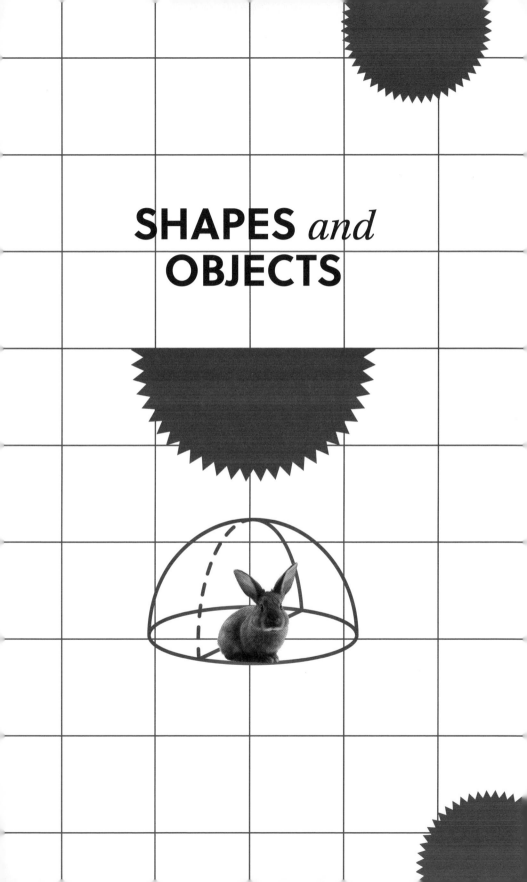

SHAPES *and* OBJECTS

The usual suspects

Here is a list of mugshots of the sorts of two-dimensional shapes and three-dimensional objects you will encounter in primary school. To assist you in your investigations, we've listed important defining characteristics. But be careful, some of these slippery characters can have two identities at once. Huh? Trust me ... let's go.

2D shapes

I should point out that two dimensions means the shape has length and breadth but no height. So you can draw it on a flat piece of paper – for example, a square. You do not need to step into the third dimension of height and come up off the piece of paper like you would with a cube, for example. We fancy pants mathematicians talk about the 2D sheets 'lying in a plane' rather than on a piece of paper. But hey, that's just us getting our jollies – a piece of paper is fine.

2D: Three-sided shapes

There's only one basic type of three-sided figure in two dimensions: the good old triangle.

The word 'triangle' comes from 'tri' = 3 – like tricycle, triple, trimester. It is a shape with three angles. We can form a triangle by drawing three points almost anywhere on a sheet of paper and joining them with straight lines.

Extension!

Triangle teaser

Draw three points and take a ruler and make a triangle. Do this a few times. Then ask your child, 'Can you draw three points that can't be joined to make a triangle?' The answer of course ... think about it a bit ... okay, I'll tell you ...

is when the three points lie on the same line. As long as one point here is even a fraction of a millimetre off the line, we are good to go and draw a triangle. But strictly we need three points that are not 'collinear' (on the same line).

There are many different types of triangles. Let's meet them.

Perhaps the most natural and elegant of the triangles occurs when all three sides are the same length. We combine the two Latin words *equi* (equal) and *latus* (side – which also gives us the word 'lateral') and call this an **equilateral** (equal-sided) **triangle**. Here is a typical example:

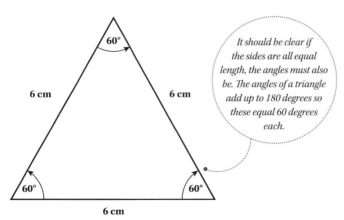

6 cm

6 cm

6 cm

60°

60°

60°

It should be clear if the sides are all equal length, the angles must also be. The angles of a triangle add up to 180 degrees so these equal 60 degrees each.

Almost as cool looking as an equilateral triangle is one with two equal sides. Using the Greek words *isos* (equal) and *skelos* (legs) we call these sorts of triangles **isosceles**. Here's one I prepared earlier:

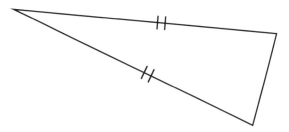

Three cool things to know about isosceles triangles:

1. The two small lines on two sides of the triangle indicate that those sides are of equal length. In our previous example, if we didn't have 6 cm written on each side, but instead had matching marks on all three sides, that would also tell us it was equilateral.
2. All equilateral triangles are, by definition, isosceles. But not all isosceles triangles are equilateral. (Try busting that out at your next dinner party.)
3. The two equal sides in an isosceles triangle also means it must have two equal angles.

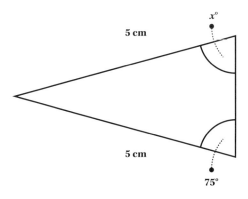

In this triangle we know $x = 75$.

This brings us to triangles with no equal sides. We call these **scalene** triangles. In saying that isosceles triangles are 'almost as cool' as equilateral triangles, I may have upset a few fans of scalene triangles. Don't get me wrong, some of my favourite triangles are scalene. If you join up three random dots on a sheet of paper you will almost always get a scalene triangle.

The three unequal sides also means that a scalene triangle has three unequal angles.

A really important family of triangles, are the **right-angled triangles** (sometimes called just **right triangles**). In a right-angled triangle, one of the angles is exactly **90°**.

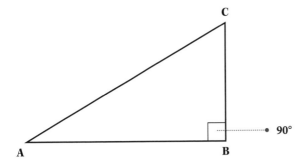

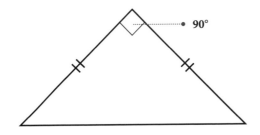

Little known fact*.
A right angle is called
a right angle because
it sits 'upright' from a
horizontal line.

*When I say 'little-
known', I mean I got to
the age of 52 without
knowing why we called
it this!

That first triangle on the previous page is a typical right-angled triangle. The square formed at the corner (we say 'vertex') B indicates that the angle there is 90°.

The second triangle shows us that there is such a thing as **'a right-angled isosceles triangle'.** It should be obvious that you cannot have a right-angled equilateral triangle.

One last thing about angles

Right angles (90° angles) are really cool and very important in geometry. If an angle is less than 90° we call it an **_acute_** angle. Angles sized between 90° to 180° are called **_obtuse_** angles.

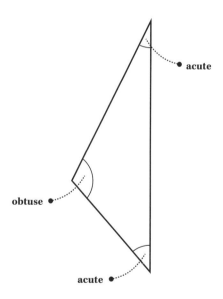

A triangle with an obtuse angle is called an obtuse-angled triangle. If all three angles are less than 90° we have an acute-angled triangle.

Extension!

Believe the hype-otenuse!

One of the most beautiful and powerful ideas in all of mathematics comes from right-angled triangles.

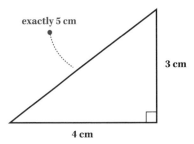

Draw a right-angled triangle with sides 3 cm and 4 cm as marked (grid paper may help). Measure the longest side (we call this the *hypotenuse*) and you will see that it is exactly 5 cm. Notice that the sides generate the equation:

$$3^2 + 4^2 = 5^2$$

We call this triple of numbers (3, 4, 5) a **Pythagorean triple**, after Pythagaros of Samos, who lived around 500 BC and was one of the great gangsta maths monsters of all time.

Check that (5, 12, 13) is a Pythagorean triple, by drawing the triangle:

Continued on next page →

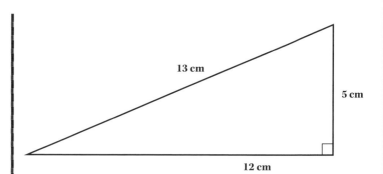

13 cm

5 cm

12 cm

Then draw the triangles represented by the triples (8, 15, 17), (7, 24, 25), (10, 24, 26), (20, 21, 29) and (16, 30, 34).

Draw some random right-angled triangles and measure them to, say, one decimal place – e.g. 3.7 cm. Convince yourself the theorem holds for all right-angled triangles. Note, with the one decimal place approximation of the side lengths a, b and c, your equation $a^2 + b^2 = c^2$ will be slightly out.

Welcome to **Pythagoras' Theorem**. He truly was a baller.

2D: Four-sided shapes

A shape with four sides (and four vertices or corners) is called a *quadrilateral – quad* meaning four, as in quadruplet or quad bike, and *latus* from Latin, still meaning side.

Joining any four dots on a sheet of paper will form a quadrilateral:

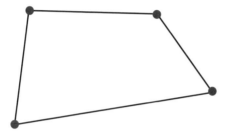

as long as you do not cross any sides over each other.

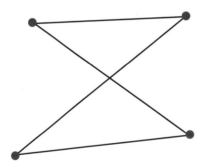

Trivia question: what if I connect 4 points, 3 that are in a straight line? Do I have a triangle or quadrilateral?

This is not part of primary school mathematics, but if you join 4 points this way you have 4 vertices (the red dots) and 4 sides. The shape also has 4 angles, one of which is 180°. It is called a DEGENERATE quadrilateral!

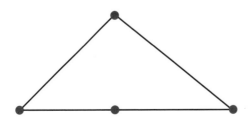

The dotted line is a ***diagonal*** of the quadrilateral. More generally, a line joining any two vertices of a two-dimensional shape is a diagonal if the vertices are not joined by an edge. So a quadrilateral clearly has two diagonals.

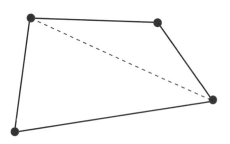

You can see that a diagonal effectively splits a quadrilateral into two triangles. The six angles of these two triangles cover exactly the four angles of the quadrilateral. The angle sum of each triangle is 180°, so **the angle sum of any quadrilateral is 2 × 180° = 360°.**

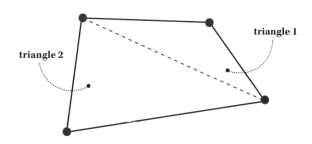

triangle 1

triangle 2

Special quadrilaterals

Parallelogram

Two lines that run perfectly alongside each other in the plane and never meet are called ***parallel lines***. A quadrilateral with two sets of parallel sides is called, not surprisingly, a ***parallelogram.***

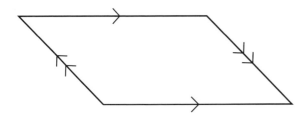

The arrows on opposite sides indicate that the sides are parallel.

A shape with at least one pair of parallel sides is called a *trapezium* (or *trapezoid*).

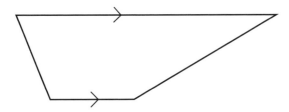

Rectangle

Now, you know what I mean when I say 'rectangle'. I know that you know what I mean when I say 'rectangle'. But when a maths nerd like me talks about a rectangle, I like to use the official definition:

A rectangle is a parallelogram with all of its angles right angles. Booyeah!

A further important and interesting property of all rectangles is that their opposite sides must be of equal length.

Square

Again, you know and I know you know, blah blah. But officially, *a square is a parallelogram with all angles and all sides equal. And ... a square is really just a special kind of rectangle, or trapezium ...*

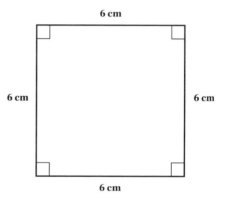

Rhombus

The final four-sided figure we will check out is the ***rhombus.***

Just imagine you had a square and you sat on it ... go with me on this. It's made of pretty sturdy stuff so it doesn't sag or bend where you plant your butt. But it does slide off to the side. Well done – you've just made a rhombus.

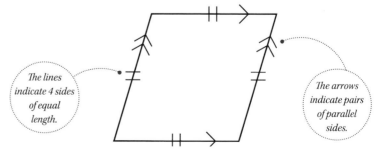

The lines indicate 4 sides of equal length.

The arrows indicate pairs of parallel sides.

A rhombus is a parallelogram, with four equal sides. It's a shape you might have described before as a diamond.

Now if it had four equal angles it would also be a square. But it clearly doesn't, once you've done your bit squashing it off to the side.

So a rhombus is not necessarily a square – because all of its angles are not equal. But strictly speaking, a square is a rhombus, because it does have all of its sides equal.

This might seem like some cute wordplay, but it goes to the heart of truly understanding the definitions of these shapes. Look back at the relevant definitions and see that the following statements about quadrilaterals are true:

- All squares, rectangles and rhombi (I know! You can use rhombuses but surely rhombi is cooler?) are parallelograms. They are also all trapezoids.
- Not all parallelograms are squares, rectangles or rhombi.
- All squares are rectangles. Not all rectangles are squares.
- All squares are rhombi. Not all rhombi are squares.
- If a rectangle is a rhombus it must also be a square.

Five sides and beyond

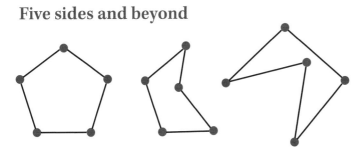

These five-sided shapes are all examples of **pentagons**. They are formed by joining five points in the plane, with no crossing sides and no collinear points.

By 'splitting' a pentagon into three triangles, we can see its angle sum must be $3 \times 180° = 540°$.

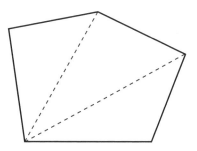

And so for a **regular pentagon** in which all sides and hence all angles are equal, we know each internal angle is equal to $\frac{540°}{5} = 108°$.

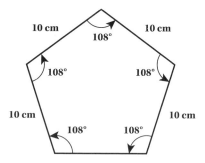

In high school, an exciting world of hexagons (six-sided shapes), octagons (eight-sided) and even dodecagons (twelve-sided – think of a 50-cent coin) opens up. But for now, that's us and two-sided shapes done.

Three-dimensional objects

As we move into three dimensions we talk about 'objects' rather than 'shapes'. Three-dimensional objects come up off our piece of paper and the objects have height as well as length and breadth. Things get a little more complicated but also, quite possibly, even more beautiful.

Let's get some terms straight from the outset:

A *polyhedron* is an object with many (*poly* – Greek) faces (*hedron* – again Greek). Here is a selfie a typical polyhedron is about to post on Instagram.

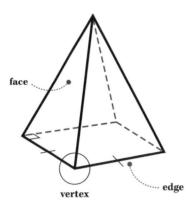

In this 3D object, which you will soon know as a **square pyramid**, we have a square *base*. We have also labelled an *edge* and a *vertex*, which is the point where two or more edges of a polyhedron meet. Each flat side of a polyhedron is called a *face*. In the same way that edges run between vertices, faces sit between edges.

As with 2D shapes, some 3D objects have special properties and names. Let's meet a few.

Regular polyhedra

A polyhedron is *regular* if all of its faces are regular polygons. Remember that regular means each side is the same length. This sounds a bit complicated, but check out these examples. The regular polyhedron with which you're probably most familiar is the good old **cube.**

Named after Ice Cube, the seminal gangsta rapper of the early 90s (not true – just checking you're paying attention), a cube has six faces, all being squares of the same size. It has eight vertices at each of which three faces meet. You should be able to count twelve edges on a cube.

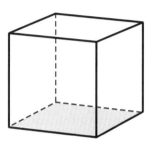

In fact, there are only five types of regular polyhedra. Named after the philosopher Plato, they are called the *Platonic Solids*. In addition to the cube, we have the:

Tetrahedron: 4 equilateral triangular faces, 6 edges, 4 vertices.

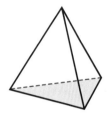

Octahedron: 8 equilateral triangular faces, 12 edges, 6 vertices.

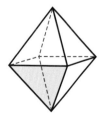

Dodecahedron: 12 regular pentagonal faces, 30 edges, 20 vertices (you might have seen these as dice in some board games).

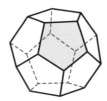

Icosahedron: 20 equilateral triangular faces, 30 edges, 12 vertices.

Let's be honest; it's hard to count the edges and vertices of these more complicated objects. But here's a great way to do it.

If you can count the 12 pentagonal faces of a dodecahedron, you should be able to see that, drawn separately, 12 pentagons would generate 12 × 5 = 60 edges. But in the dodecahedron, each edge is involved in two faces. So the 60 edges collapse down to 30 edges.

Similarly, the 12 pentagons have 12 × 5 = 60 vertices, but each vertex is the meeting of three faces. So there are 60 ÷ 3 = 20 vertices in a dodecahedron.

Apply a similar logic to the icosahedron to convince yourself of the number of sides and edges there. (Hint: you're using 20 × 3, 60 ÷ 2 and 60 ÷ 3 to assist your reasoning.)

Prism break

Next up in our parade of 3D suspects are the ***prisms***.

A prism is a polyhedron with a base and top that are the same-shaped polygon, and whose sides are parallelograms. Huh?

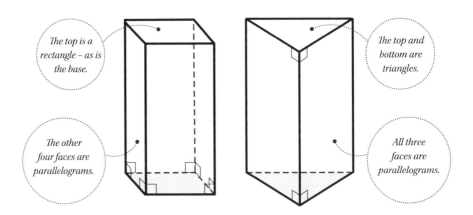

The top is a rectangle – as is the base.

The top and bottom are triangles.

The other four faces are parallelograms.

All three faces are parallelograms.

The prism on the left is called a **rectangular** prism. Looking at the labels can you see what I meant when I said, 'A prism is a polyhedron that has the same base and top (in this case a rectangle) and its other faces are all parallelograms?' On the right we have a **triangular prism**. Because the side faces stand at right angles to the base, we call them **right prisms**.

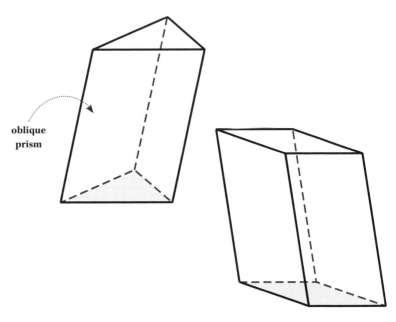

oblique prism

These two examples are also prisms. Just not right prisms. Because they are 'tilted' we call them *oblique* prisms.

Fun fact – when a right prism is tilted into an oblique prism, it keeps the same volume no matter how far we tilt it.

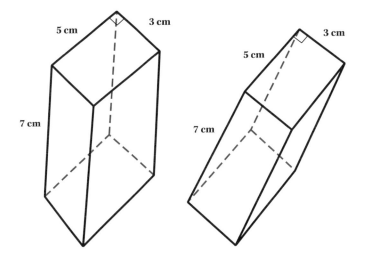

You can get a feel for this by taking a deck of cards and sliding them across like this. The volume stays the same.

A **cross-section** of a polyhedron is the two-dimensional shape you reveal by slicing through it – usually parallel or at right angles to the base. The horizontal cross-section of a triangular prism (standing on its base) is a triangle. Can you see by turning the vertical cross-section that it is a rectangle?

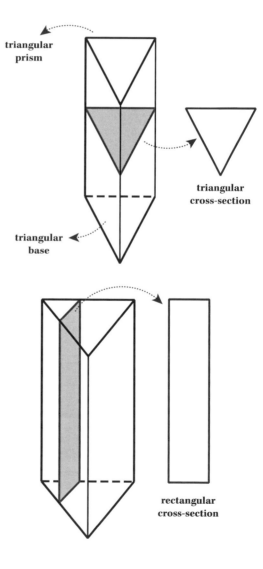

triangular prism

triangular cross-section

triangular base

rectangular cross-section

You can take angled cross-sections too. But if you just spoke of the 'cross-section' of this triangular prism it would be assumed you meant the horizontal cross-section (the triangle).

Cylinder

Right up there alongside the cube in the parade of well-known polyhedron is the good old cylinder. Whether as cans of energy drink for the younger ones or rubberised massage hip rollers for us oldies, cylinders are everywhere.

A cylinder has a circular base and top. It is **NOT** a prism, because its base and top are not polygons. The horizontal cross-section of a cylinder is a circle.

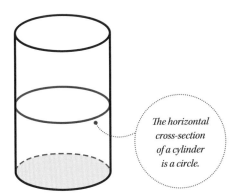

The horizontal cross-section of a cylinder is a circle.

Pyramids

A pyramid is a polyhedron. It has a polygon for a base, but while a prism has the same-shaped top, the cross-sections of a pyramid contract until we reach a point at the top. This point is called the **apex.** As a result, the faces of a pyramid that run from the edges of the base to the apex are triangular.

When it comes to pyramids, the two most commonly seen suspects are the triangular-based pyramid (a tetrahedron) and the square pyramid (like those in Egypt) as shown on the next page.

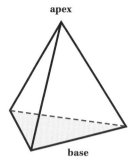
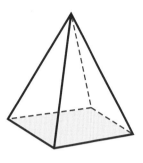

apex

base

But there is no reason why we can't have pentagonal pyramids too:

Or hexagonal pyramids:

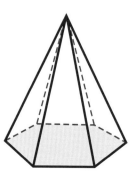

Or even a 'wow I love what you've done with the space' pyramid. Can you see that with all of these pyramids, the horizontal cross-sections are the same shape as the base?

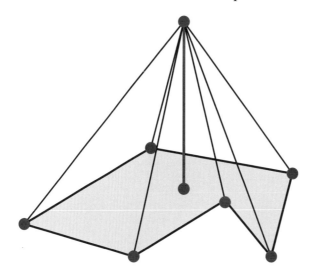

Cones

A cone has a circular base and comes to an apex.

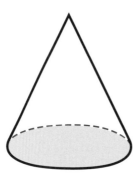

Cones are awesome, but having circular bases (not polygons) they aren't pyramids.

Nets

Can you see how the grid of squares on the left could be folded to make the cube on the right?

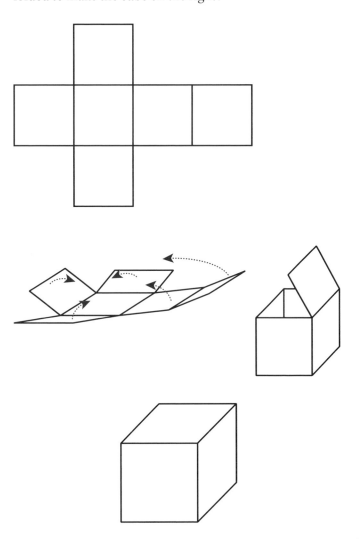

We call that grid of squares a cube **net.**

It is not the only cube net. In fact, there are 11 of them.

Fun exercise: On an A4 sheet of paper draw these nets with sides of say, 4 cm. Cut them out and fold the nets into cubes! Can you design a net for a pyramid?

The 11 nets for a cube

Every polyhedron can be 'cut' into a net.

Extension!

It's not that (Leon) hard!

Let's recall some classic 3-dimensional objects and learn a really cool fact about them (Euler's Formula).

Go back to our table of **platonic solids**. Ask your child to draw the platonic solid and to calculate again the number of faces, edges and vertices for each one. Complete this table:

Platonic solid	Verticles (V)	Faces (F)	Edges (E)

Can they spot a pattern involving the values V, F and E? While I'm asking ... can you?

Leonhard
Euler

Well, a few hundred years ago, perhaps the greatest mathematician of all time, Leonhard Euler (pronounced 'Oiler'), noticed that for every* polyhedron, V + F – E = 2. Search for other 'convex polyhedrons' online and dive deeper into this beautiful geometric fact.

* When I say 'every' – Euler's formula only applies to polyhedra that are 'convex'. This means that all the interior angles of the object are less than 180°. A concave polyhedron might look like a cube that has had a chunk cut out of one face for example. Euler's formula would not apply here.

Toughen up snowflake

Back in 1904, Swedish maths whiz Helge Von Koch introduced the world to a wonderful piece of geometry which is now called the Koch Snowflake.

To construct one, grab a ruler marked in millimetres, a pencil, a compass, a large sheet of paper and off we go.

Draw a large equilateral triangle – say 27 cm each side. (I know 27 cm sounds like a weird length to choose, but trust me).

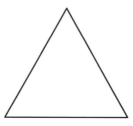

Divide each of the three sides into three lengths of 9 cm.

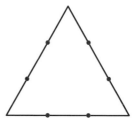

On each side, use the middle stretch of 9 cm as the base of an equilateral triangle of sides 9 cm.

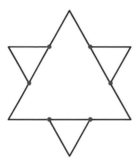

Erase the base lines of each triangle and you should have the first 'iteration' of the snowflake, like this:

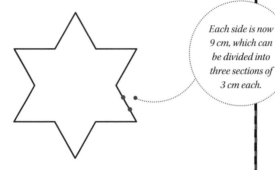

Each side is now 9 cm, which can be divided into three sections of 3 cm each.

Now divide the 12 sides into three lengths of 3 cm and use these middle lengths again as the base of a series of equilateral triangles of side lengths 3 cm.

The snowflake now has 48 edges, each of 3 cm. Let's take the next 'iteration' of the snowflake. This time divide them each into three lengths of 1 cm.

Continued on next page →

You know what to do now – use these middle sections as the bases for 48 equilateral triangles, each of side lengths 1 cm.

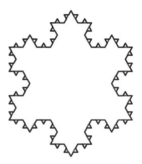

Try and picture this process going on ... forever!

As we make more and more iterations of the snowflake, its area approaches $\frac{8}{5}$ times the area of the original triangle. But the perimeter gets longer and longer ... FOREVER. **So the Koch Snowflake has a finite area, but an infinite perimeter.**

Sierpinski's Triangle

In 1915, Polish maths gun Waclaw Sierpinski got in on the triangle-based fun and created what we now call, unsurprisingly, Sierpinski's Triangle. Here it is after six iterations. By looking at the triangle can you work out how he constructed it? Give it a go yourself, using a side length for the original triangle that is a power of 2. I'd recommend 32 or, if you're really feeling lucky (and have a big enough sheet of paper), 64 cm!

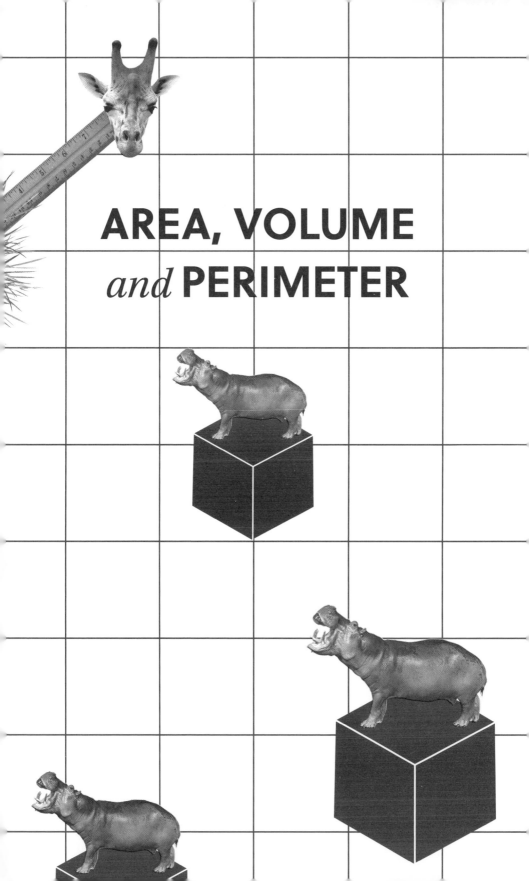

AREA, VOLUME *and* PERIMETER

The long and the short and the square and the round of it

It is important that your child knows the relationship between basic units of length; it's a life skill that will be useful. You might even need a little refresher course yourself!

1 metre = 100 centimetres (1 m = 100 cm)
One centimetre = 10 millimetres (1 cm = 10 mm)
Therefore, 1 m = 1000 mm

1 kilometre = 1000 metres (1 km = 1000 m)

You don't use it very much, but it should be obvious that:

1 km = 100,000 cm = 1,000,000 mm

When doing mathematics with various lengths, make sure you use common units.

A longer piece of timber is 1.5 m. A shorter piece is 60 cm.

You place three long pieces and two short pieces end to end. How long do they lie?

Hint: You can't add metres to centimetres, you must add similar quantities. This question doesn't say whether you must answer in metres or centimetres so you can choose either, just remember that 1.5 m = 150 cm and 60 cm = 0.6 m.

So your working could be:

$$3 \times 1.5 \text{ m} + 2 \times 60 \text{ cm} = 3 \times 150 \text{ cm} + 2 \times 60 \text{ cm} =$$
$$450 \text{ cm} + 120 \text{ cm} = 570 \text{ cm}$$

Or, working in metres:

$$3 \times 1.5 \text{ m} + 2 \times 60 \text{ cm} = 3 \times 1.5 \text{ m} + 2 \times 0.6 \text{ m} =$$
$$4.5 \text{ m} + 1.2 \text{ m} = 5.7 \text{ m}$$

How much longer are 10 short pieces laid end to end compared to $3\frac{1}{2}$ long pieces?

10 short pieces are 10×0.6 m = 6.0 m long
$3\frac{1}{2}$ long pieces are $3.5 \times 1.5 = 5.25$ m

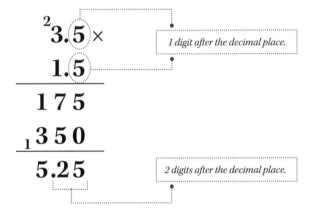

(If this isn't clear see page 162 on multiplying decimals.)

So, the 10 short pieces are 6.0 m – 5.25 m = 0.75 m or 75 cm longer.

Extension!

Turn up the nerd-meter

While we think of a metre as 100 cm or 'a long stride', the official definition is fascinating.

In 1793 the metre was first officially defined. Just after the French Revolution there was a feeling of a new future and that included doing away with old imperial units – they were a bit 'Royal' for some, and varied greatly from place to place. That's it; we were moving to the hip new thing ... decimal measurements.

A metre was decided to be one ten-millionth of the distance on the Earth's surface from the North Pole to the Equator, measured along a line passing through Paris. It seems a bit obscure, but for me it works in two ways. It is about a long human stride, so you have a natural feel for it. On a larger scale, this definition is why the circumference of the Earth around the equator is just over 40,000 kilometres!

Around a century later, a series of official metre-long bars of 90 per cent platinum and 10 per cent iridium were distributed around the world. And for almost a century these were the gold standard (or platinum-iridium standard) for defining this important length.

Over time, our ability to measure the physical world in incredible detail allowed us to move away from metre-long objects, which, while already very accurate, in theory could expand or contract over time and at

varying temperatures, and to use the atomic properties of various objects instead.

In 1960 the metre was defined in terms of the electromagnetic radiation given off by the element krypton. In 1983 it was redefined in terms of the speed of light. And in 2019 this definition was tightened up even more as part of a general overhaul of all of the basic units of measurement.

So this is how we now define a metre:

We start by defining a second. This involves some beautiful physics concerning an atom of the element caesium and a process that occurs exactly 9,192,631,770 times per second.

Once we have defined a second, a metre is officially defined by setting the distance light travels in a vacuum to be 299,792,458 metres per second!

So, there we have it. The official definition of a metre.

Area and volume

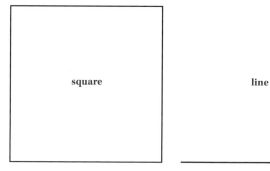

square

line

How big is this square? That's a fundamentally different question to asking how long is this line. That's because the line exists in just one direction or dimension, that is its length. But the square exists in two dimensions. It is long but it is also wide.

Let's start by looking at a very important basic square. This square has sides of 1 cm and is called a **unit square**.

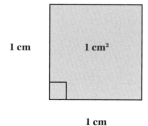

1 cm

$1\ cm^2$

1 cm

'One square centimetre' and 'one centimetre squared' mean the same thing.

The area of a unit square is **1 square centimetre,** which we also write as $1\ cm^2$.

So, you can see that this square has an area of 9 square centimetres or 9 cm²:

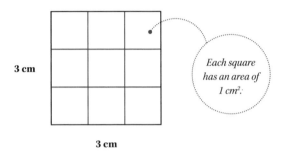

3 cm

3 cm

Each square has an area of 1 cm².

And this rectangle has an area of 8 cm² or 8 square centimetres:

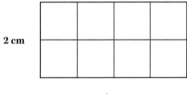

2 cm

4 cm

And can you see that to save time we could just multiply 3 × 3 or 2 × 4 respectively and get our answers without ruling up the grids?

Your child will get a better understanding of area from drawing lots of squares and rectangles to scale with a ruler and ruling up all the centimetre squares inside. After a while, the grids won't be needed, but it is great to start with them.

What about sides that aren't whole numbers?

When the sides of the shapes are not whole numbers of centimetres or metres, nothing changes. Check these out (you might want to read the section on multiplying fractions starting on page 140).

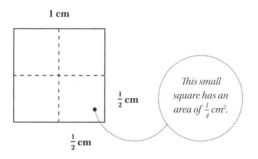

$$\tfrac{1}{2}\text{ cm} \times \tfrac{1}{2}\text{ cm} = \tfrac{1}{4}\text{ cm}^2$$

(the square is clearly $\frac{1}{4}$ of a full unit square)

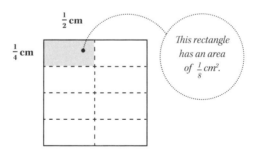

$$\tfrac{1}{2}\text{ cm} \times \tfrac{1}{4}\text{ cm} = \tfrac{1}{8}\text{ cm}^2$$

(this rectangle is clearly $\frac{1}{8}$ of a unit square)

Calculate the area of a rectangle $3\tfrac{1}{2}$ cm × 5 cm:

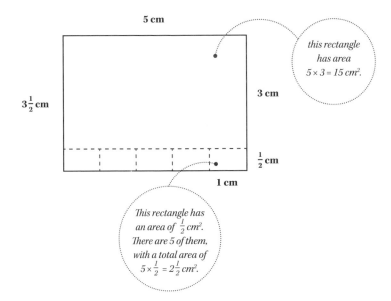

$3\frac{1}{2}$ cm

5 cm

*this rectangle
has area
$5 \times 3 = 15\ cm^2$.*

3 cm

$\frac{1}{2}$ cm

1 cm

*This rectangle has
an area of $\frac{1}{2}\ cm^2$.
There are 5 of them,
with a total area of
$5 \times \frac{1}{2} = 2\frac{1}{2}\ cm^2$.*

We can just multiply $3\frac{1}{2} \times 5 = 17\frac{1}{2}$ cm². This diagram shows that we are correct. You don't need to draw the diagrams when working out area questions. I'm just showing you here to convince you nothing changes when we move away from whole numbers as our side lengths.

Here's a tougher example:
A brick wall is 1.8 m × 3 m and features an 80 cm × 40 cm window. Draw a diagram of the wall, including the window, and calculate the area of the bricks on the wall.

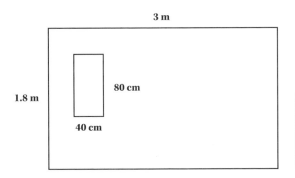

3 m

80 cm

1.8 m

40 cm

*Area = 'full wall' minus 'window'
= 3 m × 1.8 m – 0.4 m × 0.8 m
= 5.4 m² – 0.32 m²
= 5.08 m²*

More area: Triangles

Understanding the area of a square and a rectangle can help us understand the area of a triangle.

To get the area of this triangle, place it in a 4 cm × 4 cm square with grids drawn.

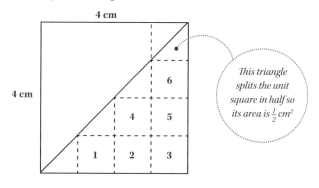

This triangle splits the unit square in half so its area is $\frac{1}{2}$ cm²

The triangle consists of six unit squares and four triangles of area $\frac{1}{2}$ cm² each.

The total area is

$$\left(6 + 4 \times \tfrac{1}{2}\right) \text{ cm}^2 = 8 \text{ cm}^2$$

We can see the area is 8 cm².

Now draw the same triangle in the same square with no grid drawn. Can you see the triangle obviously takes up exactly half of the square?

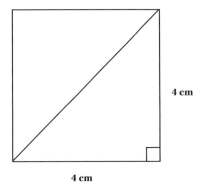

The area of the square is 4 cm × 4 cm = 16 cm², so the area of the triangle is $\frac{1}{2}$ × 4 cm × 4 cm = 8 cm²

Similarly the area of this triangle is $\frac{1}{2}$ × 4 cm × 7 cm = 14 cm².

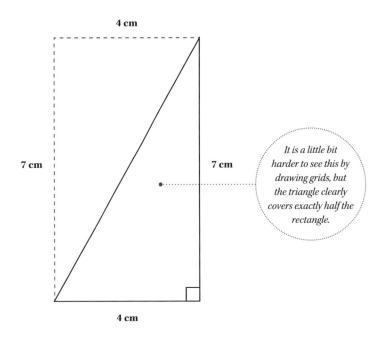

It is a little bit harder to see this by drawing grids, but the triangle clearly covers exactly half the rectangle.

More generally, the area of any right-angled triangle is A = $\frac{1}{2}$ × base × height, which we often write as A = $\frac{1}{2}$ × b × h. Note that the height 'h' is the 'perpendicular height', or the height of a line from the top of the triangle that makes a 90-degree angle with the base of the triangle.

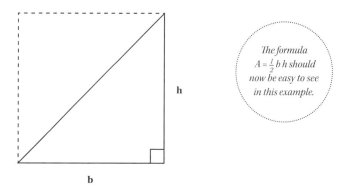

The formula A = $\frac{1}{2}$ b h should now be easy to see in this example.

'What about different shaped triangles?' I hope I hear you ask.

Look at these diagrams and you can see the formula still works:

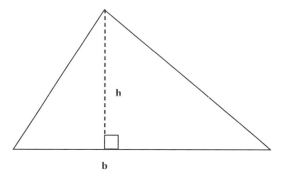

This triangle has base 'b' and perpendicular height 'h', but it is not a right-angled triangle.

Consider it sitting in a rectangle of sides b and h.

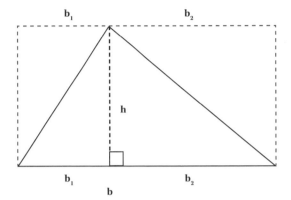

If we think of the original triangle as two right-angled triangles joined together, it should be obvious that the two smaller right-angled triangles are each half the area of the rectangles they lie within. So the whole triangle is half the area of the bigger rectangle. So again, Area = $\frac{1}{2}$ × b × h.

I will do this final example numerically so as not to blindside you with algebra. But it works for triangles of any size.

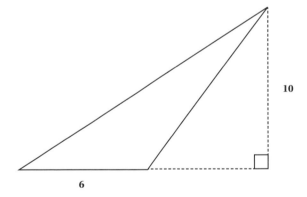

Here, the top of the triangle lies 'outside of the base'. Don't panic! Again, consider it inside a bigger rectangle. Say the top of the triangle sits 8 units further away from the end of the base.

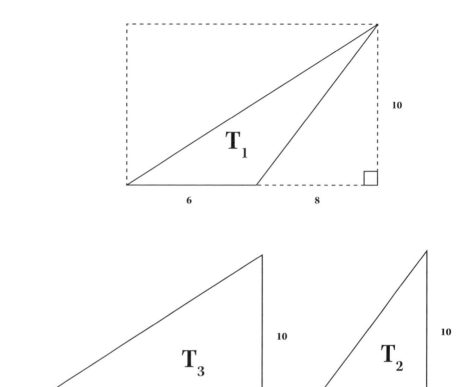

Label our triangle T_1 as above

When it comes to the areas of the triangles, clearly
$T_1 + T_2 = T_3$

But, $T_2 = \frac{1}{2} \times 8 \times 10 = 40$ units^2 and $T_3 = \frac{1}{2} \times 14 \times 10 = 70$ units^2.

So, $T_1 = 30$ units^2.

And if we had used our formula to calculate the area T_1 we would have got:

Area $= \frac{1}{2} \times b \times h = \frac{1}{2} \times 6 \times 10 = 30$ units^2.

So, this gorgeous formula holds for all types of triangles.

We can also use it as a part of more complicated questions. For example:

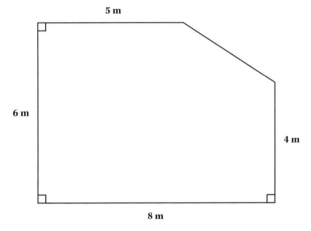

This shape can be thought of as a rectangle with a triangle removed. And we can reconstruct that relationship to help work out the area.

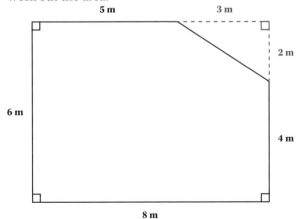

Area (our shape)
= Area (rectangle)
– Area (triangle)
$= 6\,m \times 8\,m - \frac{1}{2} \times 2\,m \times 3\,m$
$= 48\,m^2 - 3\,m^2$
$= 45\,m^2$

Volume of solids

When we look at the size of three-dimensional figures, we see that they enclose a space. Like the amount of space inside of a cereal box or the amount of water you could put into a swimming pool.

Volume measures how much space a three-dimensional shape contains, and we often label these three dimensions length, width and height, like on this box or '**rectangular prism**'.

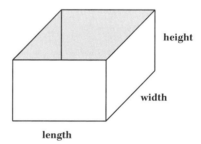

In the same way the basic unit of length, the centimetre, generated a unit square of area 1 cm², it also generates a unit cube of volume 1 cm³. We usually pronounce this 'one cubic centimetre', but 'one centimetre cubed' means the same thing.

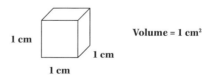

So to work out the volume of the rectangular prism opposite of length 3 cm, width 6 cm and height 2 cm, we are asking how many cubic centimetres would fit inside the box.

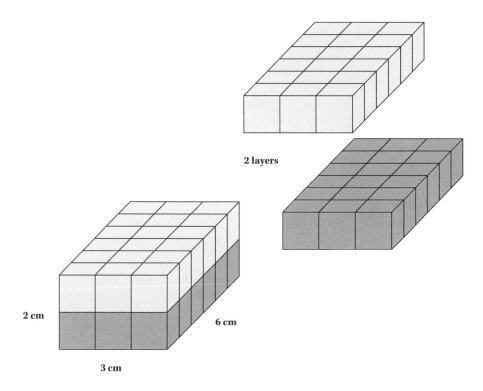

2 layers

2 cm

6 cm

3 cm

You should be able to see that we could place a 3 × 6 layer of cubic centimetres into the box and place a second layer on top. The volume of the box is:

$$3 \times 6 \times 2 \text{ cm}^3 = 36 \text{ cm}^3$$

More generally, the volume of a prism like this is given by the formula:

$$V = l \times w \times h$$

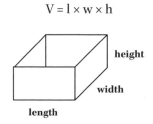

height

width

length

Here is a tough example for you:

Winona Wagstaff was a walker from Wellington. Her home town was so proud of her efforts they erected a giant W in her honour. It was massive.

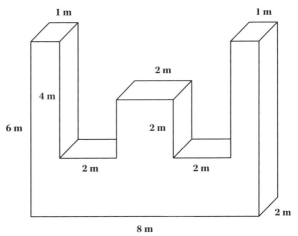

What volume of concrete in cubic metres would be needed to create the Big W?

The Big W can be thought of as the front face, moving back through a depth of 2 m.

And the front face can be split up into these five smaller shapes:

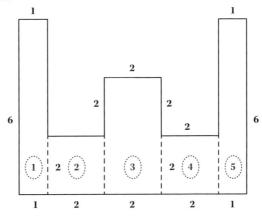

So the area of the front W is $6 \times 1 + 2 \times 2 + 4 \times 2 + 2 \times 2 + 6 \times 1 = 28$ m².

Giving us a volume of $28 \times 2 = 56$ m³.

Litres and millilitres

The other volume questions your child will encounter in primary school concern the volume of liquids, sometimes called capacity. The rules are exactly the same, but because we are dealing with measurements that we don't use as often as centimetres and metres, things can get a little confusing.

It's really important to understand the basic units.

We are all familiar with a litre. You can show your child a one-litre milk bottle and compare it to a two-litre bottle, or 1.5 litres of soda water. Now show them a smaller can of soft drink or a cardboard container of juice. It might be labelled 375 ml. What are 'ml'?

One litre = 1000 millilitres (1 L = 1000 ml)

It helps to remember that there are 1000 millimetres in a metre. This can remind your child that 1000 ml makes 1 litre. But it gets confusing when we talk about the size of a millilitre:

One millilitre of water fills one cubic CENTIMETRE!!! and weighs one gram.

This confuses children greatly. Why isn't it one cubic millimetre?

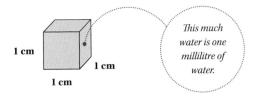

1 cm

1 cm

1 cm

This much water is one millilitre of water.

I found with my daughters it really helped to keep bringing this back to practical examples.

Looking in my fridge as I write this I can see two 1-litre liquid containers that are both rectangular prisms (yep, that's what I see when I look in the fridge!).

Measuring them both, you can see the relationship between 1 litre and 1000 cm³.

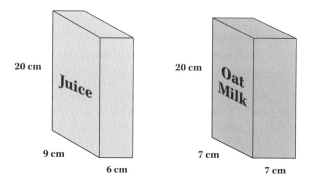

For the juice pack, 6 cm × 9 cm × 20 cm = just over 1000 cm³ (the exact values here are not important. Can they see it is very close to 1000?).

For the oat milk, 7 cm × 7 cm × 20 cm = 49 × 20 ... which is almost exactly 50 × 20 = 1000 cm³.

Your child should not get a ruler out and run to the fridge every time they want to remember how big a millilitre is. But just guessing roughly the size of a litre of milk should get them close.

If a millilitre was a cubic millimetre, then a litre would be incredibly small.

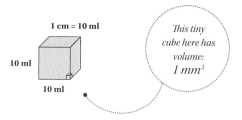

1 cm = 10 ml

10 ml

10 ml

This tiny cube here has volume: 1 mm³

Can you see that 10 × 10 × 10 = 1000, so 1000 mm^3 is only 1 cm^3, which is way smaller than a litre. I don't want to labour the point, but these basic facts, that 1 L = 1000 cm^3 and that 1 ml = 1 cm^3 are the things that most confuse kids about liquid volume. Get them right and you are well on the way.

Convert 15,000 millilitres into litres:
$$15,000 \text{ ml} = 15 \times 1000 \text{ ml} = 15 \text{ L}$$

Convert 3.25 litres into millilitres:
$$3.25 \text{ L} = 3.25 \times 1000 \text{ ml} = 3250 \text{ ml}$$

Again, this last question should make sense. Two 1.5-litre bottles of soda (3 L) look like they would be about the same as ten 375 ml cans (3750 ml). It's not exactly the same, but it's not out by a factor of 10 or 100, which is easy to do if you get basic units of volume confused.

One kilolitre = 1000 litres

Again, this follows the unit kilo = 1000 as in 1000 m = 1 kilometre and 1 kilogram = 1000 grams.

Tough question

A local swimming pool is 1.5 m deep, 15 m wide and 50 m long. How many kilolitres does it hold?

Litres are defined in terms of centimetres. So, it's best we change all the metres in the question into centimetres and go from there. It's really important here to keep track of all the zeroes and not 'lose' any. They may not seem like much, but being out by a single zero can make our answer 10 times bigger or smaller than what we want!

Tough question!

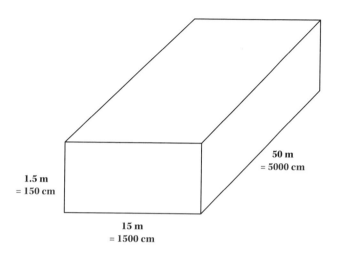

The volume of the pool is 150 × 1500 × 5000
= 1,125,000,000 cm³!

= 1,125,000,000 millitres = 1,125,000 litres = 1125 kilolitres

Perimeter

The Greek words *peri* (around) and *metron* (measure) give us **perimeter**, which is the measure of how far it is around the edge of a two-dimensional shape.

The perimeter of this triangle is 4 + 5 + 8 = 17 m.

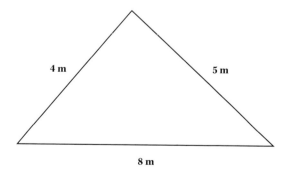

Cutting into a figure can reduce its area, but for perimeter we just keep adding the lengths.

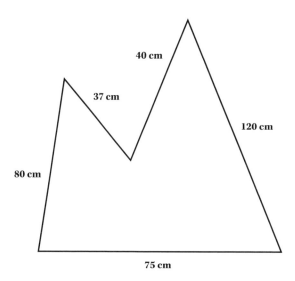

Perimeter = 75 + 120 + 40 + 37 + 80 = 352 cm

The question does not need to give us every side length for us still to be able to calculate perimeter. Check out these two examples:

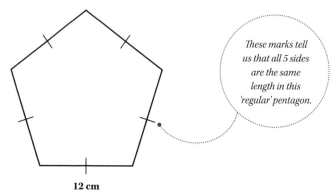

These marks tell us that all 5 sides are the same length in this 'regular' pentagon.

Perimeter = 5 × 12 cm = 60 cm

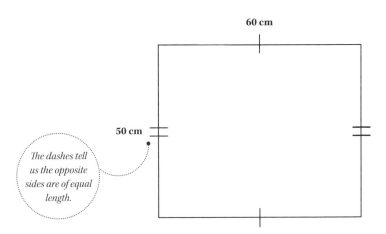

The dashes tell us the opposite sides are of equal length.

Perimeter = 60 + 50 + 60 + 50 = 220 cm

One final classic question type. Compare the areas and perimeters of these two shapes:

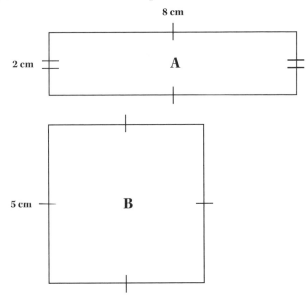

Make sure you use the same units for each comparison.

Shape A: Perimeter = 2 cm + 8 cm + 2 cm + 8 cm = 20 cm
Area = 2 cm × 8 cm = 16 cm²

Shape B: Perimeter = 5 cm + 5 cm + 5 cm + 5 cm = 20 cm
Area = 5 × 5 cm = 25 cm²

Shapes A and B have the same perimeter but enclose different areas.

And these two:

Again, make sure you use the same units.

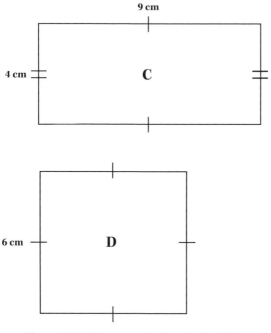

Shape C: Perimeter = 4 + 9 + 4 + 9 = 26 cm
Area = 4 × 9 = 36 cm²

Shape D: Perimeter = 4 × 6 cm = 24 cm
Area = 6 × 6 cm = 36 cm²

Shapes C and D have different perimeters but enclose the same area.

Get those units right!

It's really important that students write the correct units to their answers in these topic areas.

Nothing is more frustrating than doing all the hard work and answering '25' but losing half a mark because the teacher needed to see '25 m²'. Or for a student to answer an area question in cm³ which makes no sense.

So remember the relationship between what we are measuring and the respective units.

Perimeter is length so is measured in length units: cm, m, km, etc.

Area is measured in square units: cm², km², etc.

Volume is a cubic measurement and so is measured in cm³, m³, etc.

Litres, millilitres and kilolitres imply volume. So we only say 20 litres, we do NOT say '20 litres cubed'.

After all that you might need a refreshing beverage. I leave the content (and the volume) to your discrection.

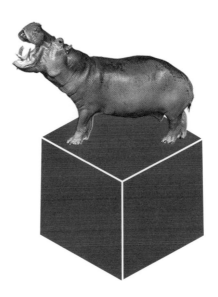

A FEW
QUICK BITES

AVERAGES

In primary school, students study statistics and probability from the early years. It is in the last couple of years of primary and in early secondary that some pretty gnarly words get thrown around: frequency, tally, value and the '3 Ms': median, mode and mean.

Here are a couple of examples that best show the first three, then we will get down to some definitions for the other three.

There are 21 people in Sahara's class. Her teacher asked the class to record how many people in their household played regular team sport. The answers were as follows:

0, 1, 1, 0, 3, 3, 0, 2, 1, 5, 3, 2, 2, 2, 2, 1, 0, 1, 2, 3, 2

We can write the results up in this **'frequency table'**:

Value/Score	Tally	Frequency

Value (or score) is a particular result of the activity.

Tally is used to keep count as you read off each value.

Frequency is the number of times a value occurs.

Score	Tally	Frequency
0	||||	4
1	⊬⊦⊦	5
2	⊬⊦⊦ ||	7
3	||||	4
4		0
5	|	1

Every 5 scores we put a cross line through to make counting easier.

4 + 5 + 7 + 4 +1 = 21
The number of students in the class

When you add up the values in the frequency column you get the number of scores; in this case, the 21 students in the class. If these numbers don't match, you've made a mistake!

The **mode** of a set of data is **the value with the highest frequency**. It is, in effect, the most popular value. In this case there are 7 households with 2 playing regular team sport, making 2 the mode for this survey.

The **median** of a group of values is **the score that lies in the middle when we write them from least to greatest**. So to find the middle value of these scores, we could rearrange them in the order:

0, 0, 0, 0, 1, 1, 1, 1, 1, 2, 2, 2, 2, 2, 2, 2, 3, 3, 3, 3, 5

Counting in from each end, we can see that the middle score is:

~~0, 0, 0, 0, 1, 1, 1, 1, 1, 2,~~ ...(2)... ~~2, 2, 2, 2, 2, 3, 3, 3, 3, 5~~

So the median is 2.

Two important things here:
1. The median and the mode do not have to be the same value. Draw up a frequency table and convince yourself that with the values:

    0, 1, 5, 6, 1, 1, 9, 3, 1, 2, 7 – the mode is 1 but the median score is 2.

2. The mode will always be one of the scores in the data. The median does not have to be. To get the median of the 10 scores:

    1, 1, 2, 3, 4, 5, 6, 11, 18, 19

We see that because the number of scores is even, there is no single 'middle score'.

1, 1, 2, 3, (4, 5) 6, 11, 18, 19

In this case we take the halfway point between, or average of, 4 and 5 and get a median of $\frac{4+5}{2} = \frac{9}{2}$.

Again, the median was not one of the values in our survey.

I didn't mean to be mean

Now that we understand median and mode, it's time for the third 'M word' **mean.** The mean, sometimes called the **average**, lets us understand how a set of data is distributed. To calculate the mean we use the formula:

$$\textbf{Mean} = \frac{\textbf{sum of the values}}{\textbf{number of values}} \textbf{ which is sometimes written}$$

$$\textbf{as } \frac{\textbf{sum of the scores}}{\textbf{number of scores}} \textbf{ or even just as } \frac{\textbf{sum}}{\textbf{number}}$$

So, the mean or the average of the

numbers 10, 13, 8, 9 and 15 is

$$\frac{10 + 13 + 8 + 9 + 15}{5} = \frac{55}{5} = 11$$

and for the numbers 1.8, 2.3, 0.9 and 3.6 is

$$\frac{1.8 + 2.3 + 0.9 + 3.6}{4} = \frac{8.6}{4} = 2.15$$

The average doesn't have to be a score that was possible to achieve in the particular data set we are examining. Ricky Ponting's batting average in Test Cricket was 51.85 runs per innings, even though it's impossible to score 51.85 in an innings. Similarly, when you read that in 2018 the Australian birth rate was 1.74 babies per woman, no one is out there having 0.74 of a baby!

One other thing

Some data sets have a mode but no median or mean. For example, if we measured the meals chosen in a canteen in a given lunchtime, we can see that sushi was the most popular choice and is therefore the mode. But there is no sensible way to order these categories from smallest to greatest. Nor can you tell me what the average of a bread roll and a piece of sushi would be (except that it would taste AWESOME!).

Fruit	12
Bread roll	16
Sushi	22
Soup	14
Milk	17

Extension!

Calculating the median for larger data sets

If we have a large amount of scores it can be impractical to list all the scores from least to greatest.

'So how do we calculate the median, Adam?' – I like to kid myself you are asking. Well, curious reader, alongside the frequency column, we can create a 'cumulative frequency' column. The cumulative frequency of a score measures the frequency of that score and all smaller scores. It helps us locate the median score quickly.

Score	Frequency	Cumulative frequency
0	14	14
1	14	28
2	7	35
3	13	48
4	8	56
5	9	65

There are 14 + 14 = 28 scores of 1 or 0.

Score 33 is 'in here' so the median score is 2.

There are 65 scores in total. So the middle score is 33rd on the list (it has 32 below and 32 scores above it).

Note here the scores 0 and 1 both have the greatest frequency (14). So this data set has two modes, 0 and 1. It is called a 'bi-modal' data set.

Score	Frequency	Cumulative frequency
10	4	4
12	7	11
14	12	23
16	19	42
18	11	53
20	7	60

When we list the scores in order from least to greatest scores, 30 and 31 are both 16.

The median score is 16.

But with this data:

Score	Frequency	Cumulative frequency
0	12	12
3	18	30
6	15	45
9	15	60

There are 60 scores in total. If we listed them from least to greatest they would split into two equal groups of 30 scores. So the median is the average of the 30th and 31st score.

Score 30 = 3

Score 31 = 6

The median score = $\frac{3+6}{2}$ = 4.5.

There are 60 scores in total so again we must average scores 30 and 31 to get the median.

Nothing but net

One of the tougher questions students can be asked on averages, and which sometimes features on selective school examinations and the like, might be this:

Peter set himself the challenge of averaging 30 points a game across the six-game series. In the first 5 games he scored 24, 28, 42, 21 and 26. What is he averaging after 5 games? What will he need to score in the final game to meet his challenge?

After 5 games, his average was;

$$\text{Average} = \frac{\text{total score}}{\text{number of scores}} = \frac{24 + 28 + 42 + 21 + 26}{5} = \frac{141}{5}$$

= 28.2 points per game

After 6 games, for his average to be 30, we would have:

$$\text{Average} = \frac{\text{total score}}{\text{number of scores}}$$

$$30 = \frac{\text{total score}}{6}$$

So his total score for the 6 games would have to be 30 × 6 = 180 points.

After 5 games he has 141 points. So in the 6th game he needs to score 180 − 141 = 39 points.

The following diagrams will help your thinking.

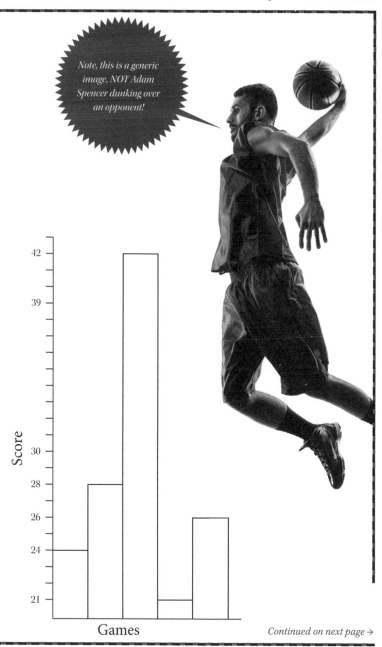

Continued on next page →

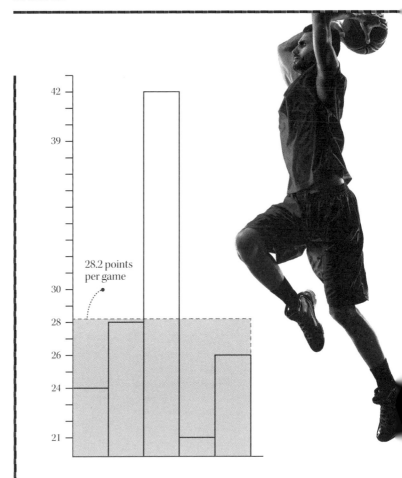

After 5 games Peter averaged 28.2 points. I picture
this as a rectangle showing him scoring exactly 28.2
points per game (impossible, I know!).

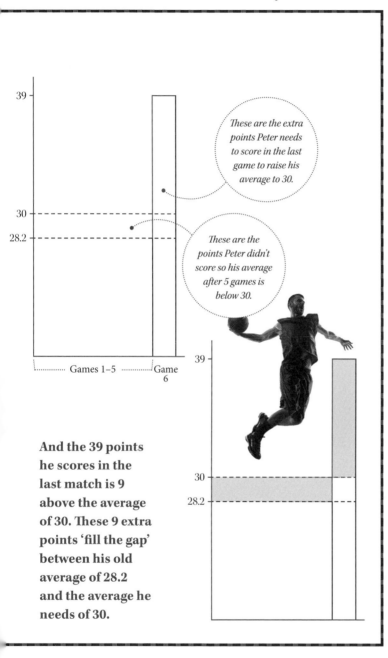

These are the extra points Peter needs to score in the last game to raise his average to 30.

These are the points Peter didn't score so his average after 5 games is below 30.

Games 1–5   Game 6

39

30
28.2

And the 39 points he scores in the last match is 9 above the average of 30. These 9 extra points 'fill the gap' between his old average of 28.2 and the average he needs of 30.

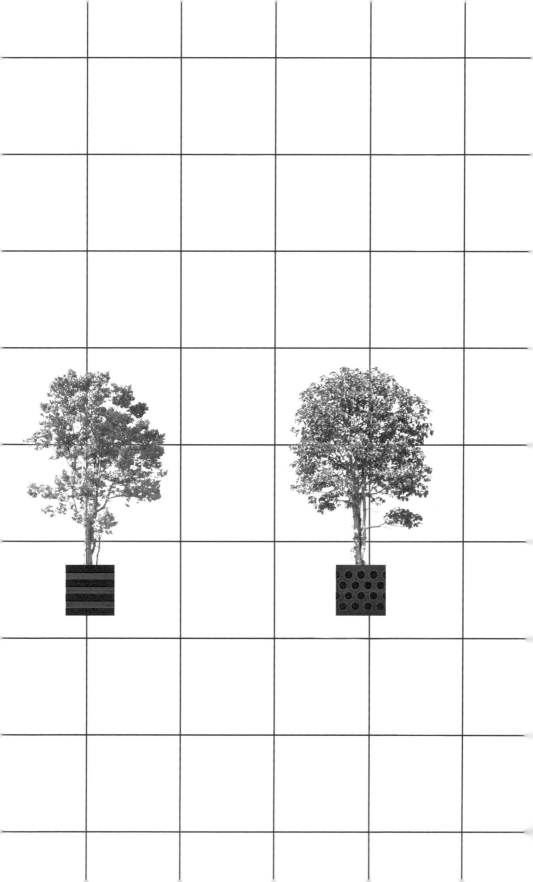

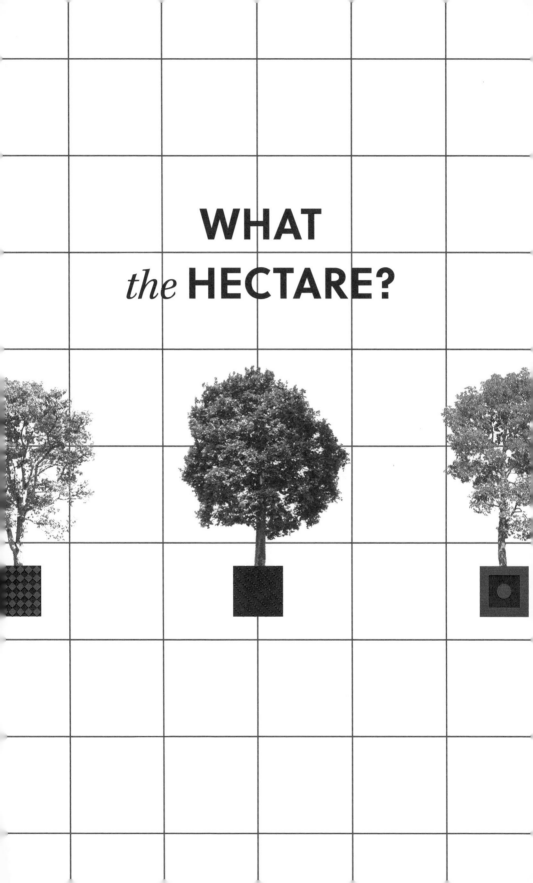

WHAT
the HECTARE?

I love mathematics and I love teaching it. If you ask me what's my favourite part of primary school maths, well that's like asking a parent which child they love the most. But I'll be completely honest, when I stumble across the obligatory question on hectares, much like when I see a payphone or realise that Nickelback have just released another album, part of me thinks, 'Well, that is a blast from the past.'

Anyway, let's meet a form of measurement I like to call 'the big h-a' – I'm talking hectares.

Square centimetres are awesome for describing the area of, say, a dinner plate, or a sheet of paper.

Square metres are great for measuring a backyard (remember them?) or, say, a netball court or football field.

Square kilometres are great for measuring the size of a state or country. We could still use square centimetres, but saying Australia is 7,692,024 km^2 just feels better than the equally accurate 76,920,240,000,000,000 cm^2.

But what about dealing with areas that are big, but not gigantic? When it comes to describing something bigger than a netball court, but smaller than, say, Queensland, we sometimes use hectares, which are abbreviated to ha.

A hectare is 10,000 m², which is the area of a
square 100 metres × 100 metres

**A field is 250 metres × 600 metres. What is its area in
hectares?**

The area of the field is 250 m × 600 m = 150,000 m²

Dividing 150,000 by 10,000 (comparing the number of
zeroes is a good way), we see that the area of the field is
150,000 m² = 15 × 10,000 m² or 15 hectares.

Convert 4.025 hectares into square metres:

4.025 ha = 4.025 × 10,000 m² = 40,250m²

And that, dear reader, is pretty much all you need to know
about hectares. Any questions, hit me up via a fax machine
... or maybe a carrier pigeon.

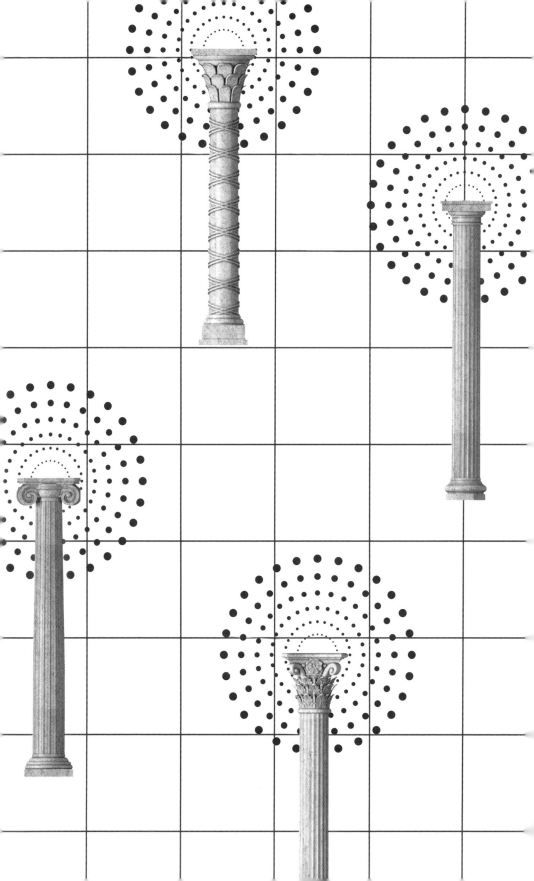

Roman
NUMERALS

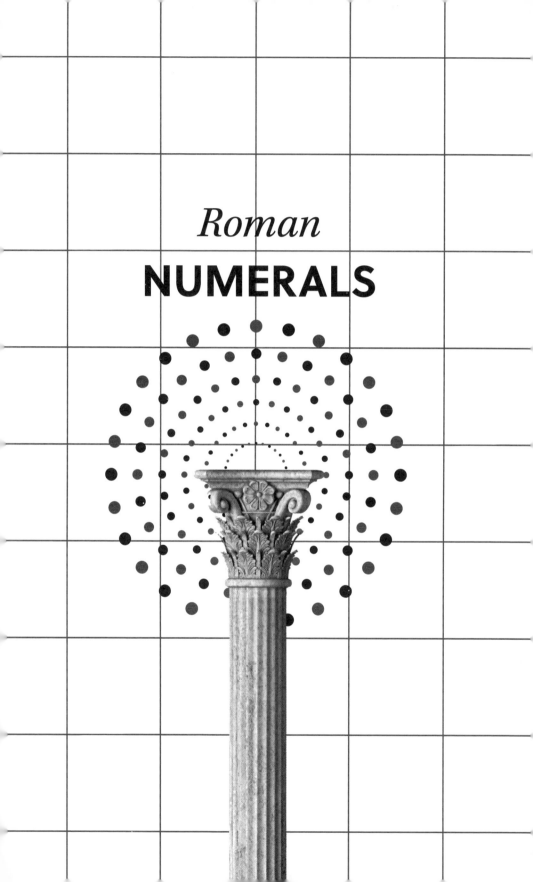

Okay I'll be completely honest here ... I'm not quite sure why Roman numerals are still taught at school. Yes it's good to learn a new way of thinking and to understand that different cultures have used different numbers over time. But, let's be honest, except for looking at the Town Hall clock and saying 'oh, it's 5 pm' or watching the credits of *Gone with the Wind* and saying 'wow that film was made in MCMXXXIX ... that means 1939', they don't pop up all that often.

Anyway sometimes you've just gotta go with the flow ... here's a quick primer on Roman numerals.

The value of the letters are:

I = 1, V = 5, X = 10, L = 50, C = 100, D = 500 and M = 1000

And generally we write the symbols from highest to lowest, left to right. So:

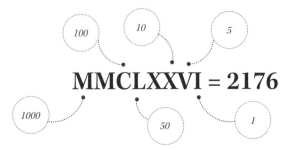

The one big and confusing exception to this is a shorthand used in Roman numerals to save time and make numbers look less ugly. The problem when you're looking at this for the first time (or desperately trying to remember it 30 years on!) is that it initially makes things look far more ugly! Rather than write IIII for 4, the Romans wrote IV. Here, the I = 1, being less than the V = 5, is subtracted.

We only ever subtract one smaller term from the larger one. So we don't write IIV for 3, we just write III. We also only ever subtract the term immediately smaller. So we do NOT write 95 as VC (100 – 5). We write 95 as:

XCV

90   5

It looks a bit ugly, but over time you get used to it.

Convince yourself that:
DCIV = 604
LXXIX = 79
and CDXLVII = 447
and you should be
ready to go.

So MCMLIX = 1959

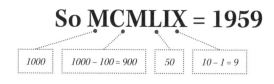

| 1000 | 1000 – 100 = 900 | 50 | 10 – 1 = 9 |

MCMIL = 1949

| 1000 | 1000 – 100 = 900 | 50 – 1 = 49 |

1999 is not MIM
it is MCMXCIX

| 1000 | 1000 – 100 = 900 | 100 – 10 = 90 | 10 – 1 = 9 |

Roman numerals grew out of the number system of the Etruscans (a civilisation in what is now Italy, around 900BC, which was eventually taken over by the Romans). They used |, ∧, ✕, ↑ and ✳ for 1, 5, 10, 50 and 100, but wrote their numbers right to left so 357 would be written ‖∧ ... 1↑✳✳✳ + 1 + 5 + 50 + 100 + 100 + 100 = 357, pretty cool hey!

The Romans were advanced engineers, building everything from giant water systems called aqueducts to huge arenas known as ampitheatres. They did all of this, without a symbol for the number 0. Check out page 308 to see where 0s finally came from.

Interesting fact 1

Interesting fact 2

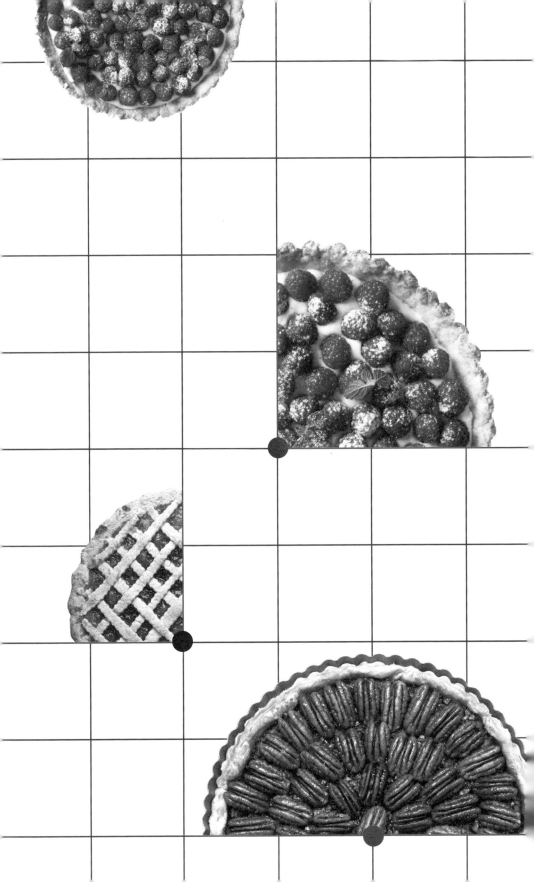

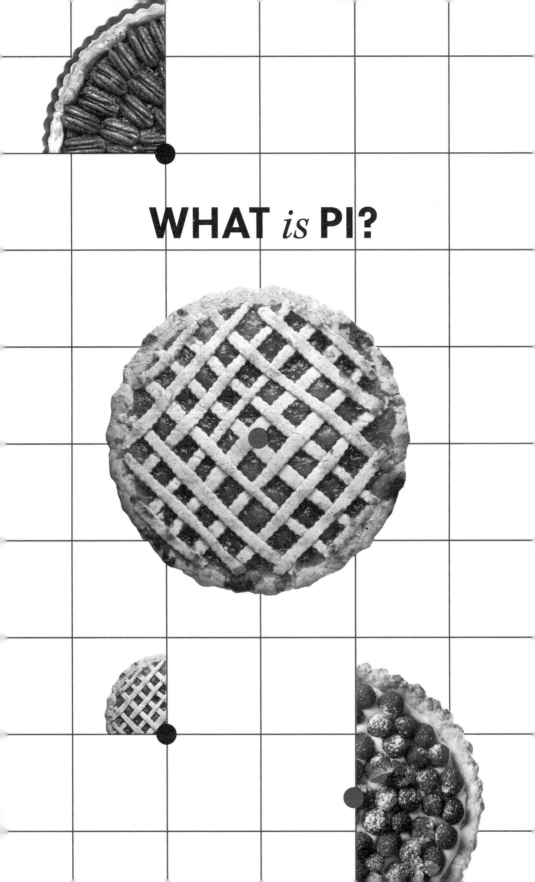

WHAT *is* PI?

Rectangles and triangles come in all sorts of sizes. But squares and circles are a bit different. All squares are essentially the same shape – just enlargements or contractions of each other. If you think about it, if you had two square pieces of cardboard of completely different sizes, you could hold the smaller one closer to you and it would perfectly cover the larger one.

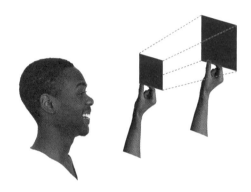

All squares are essentially the same shape. It's just the scale that changes.

Can you see it's exactly the same for circles?

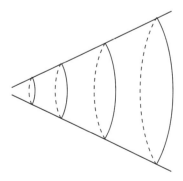

So, when we want to describe the shape of a triangle, we need to know the length of a few sides or the size of the angles between them. To understand a rectangle, we need to know its length and its breadth. But for a square we just need to know the length of one side and we know the size of the square, its area and its **perimeter** (the distance around the outside).

With a circle, it is similar. To know the full box and dice about a circle's size, all we need to know is the length across the middle of the circle.

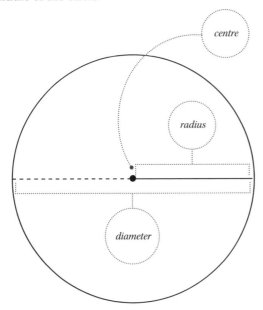

Take a compass and draw a series of circles. Then, using a plastic tape measure or a piece of string, measure the distance around the circle (the **circumference**). Compare that to the distance across each circle from one side to the other, going through the centre (the **diameter**).

Circle number	Diameter	Circumference	circumference diameter
1			
2			
3			
4			
5			

Your answers will not be exactly the same each time because it's impossible to align the tape or string perfectly with the circle. But, with a bit of practice (and patience), you should be able to get results for the value of:

Circumference divided by diameter = 3 'and a bit'

If you're crushing this exercise, maybe around 3.1.

Well, it turns out that because every circle is exactly the same shape, the distance around a circle divided by the distance across the circle is always exactly the same.

We call this amount π – otherwise known as 'pi'!

Mathematicians wanted to know the value of π a little bit more accurately than 'three and a bit', so using a variety of methods we have got better and better approximations of this incredible quantity.

It turns out π is not a number that can be written as a fraction or a decimal that terminates or repeats. π = 3.14159265359 ... and the decimal expansion continues ... forever, without ever falling into a pattern. Such a number is called **irrational** because you can't write it as a ratio i.e. a fraction.

Here are two ways that we have calculated the value of π.

1. Geometrically

We can see that the area of the circle is 'trapped' between the area of the smaller and larger hexagon. If we improved the figure from a six-sided hexagon to a 12-sided dodecagon the error would be less. As we increase the number of sides of the shape we are using inside and outside the circle, we home in more and more accurately on the area of the circle, which gives us a value for π.

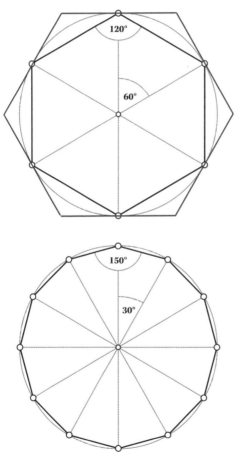

2. Mathematicians also use gorgeous formula (well I think they are gorgeous), like this:

$$\frac{1}{\pi} = \frac{1}{426880\sqrt{10005}} \sum_{k=0}^{\infty} \frac{(6k)!(13591409 + 545140134k)}{(3k)!(k!)^3(-640320)^{3k}}$$

And the larger and larger values of k you plug into the formula, the better our approximation of π.

On 29 January 2020, just before the world went into COVID lockdown, computer guru Tim Mullican computed π to ... 50 trillion decimal places!

$\frac{22}{7}$ and 3.14

In high school students will often use $\frac{22}{7}$ or 3.14 in place of π when working with circles. It is important to understand that $\frac{22}{7}$ **and 3.14 are not exact values for π.**

These are handy **approximations** for π and get you close enough for most measurements that you might need, but they are not exact values of π. As I said earlier, we have known for a long time that π, written out as a decimal, goes forever and ever. It never stops!

Cool fact

Every school has one kid who has impressively remembered π to 200 decimal places, while some true numbers nerds have successfully recited it to thousands of decimal places without notes!!! When NASA is landing a probe on a comet, sending a rover to Mars, or communicating with spacecraft millions of kilometres away, they use π to just 3.141592653589793.

Taken to 15 decimal places, if you estimated the circumference of a circle 40 billion kilometres across, stretching out to well beyond the edges of our solar system, you'd be out by 4 cm at most!

Extension!

Yummy pizza pi

What is better value? A 36 cm pizza for $20 or TWO 24 cm pizzas for $20?

The formula for the area of a circle is $\pi \times r^2$. This isn't primary school mathematics, but your child will encounter it soon enough in high school.

So, a 36 cm pizza, with radius 18 cm has area $\pi \times 18 \times 18 = 324\,\pi$ cm^2.

A 24 cm pizza has area $\pi \times 12^2 = 144\,\pi$ cm^2 and two such pizzas have area $288\,\pi$ cm^2.

The single 36 cm pizza is the better value.

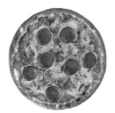

versus

36 cm   24 cm   24 cm

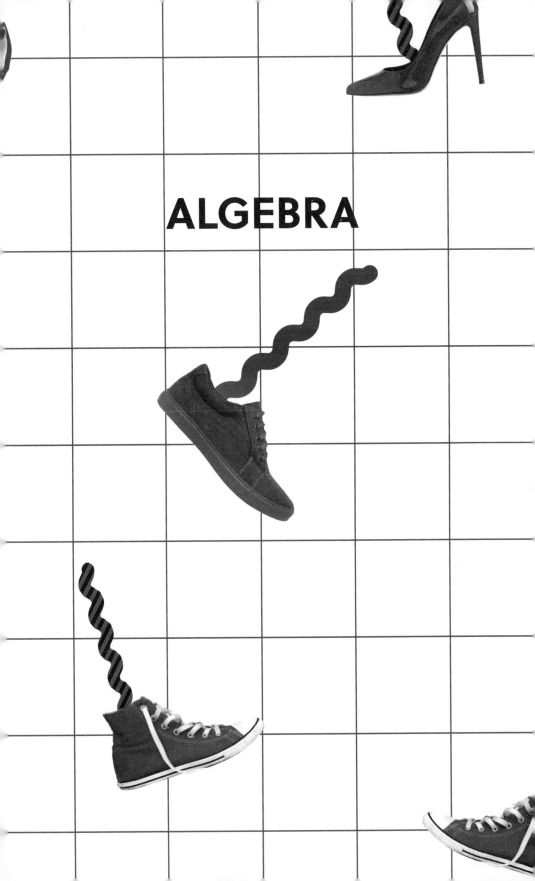

ALGEBRA

Okay here we go. I've met so many people who have said to me 'I was cool with maths ... until the numbers became letters. Then you lost me!' This one's for you!

Replacing numbers with letters takes us into the world of **algebra**. It's mainly reserved for high school study, but it does come up near the very end of primary school. It's nowhere near as scary as it might first look, and I can't stress how important it is for students who want to do well in mathematics in high school to have a solid grasp of algebra from the get-go.

All through primary school your child has been building up to algebra. Arithmetic, measurement, algorithms for addition and subtraction are all really algebra. Algebra is a language, a way of describing something in general.

Let's try this. If I told you that:

You have some pencils in your hand. I have 3 pencils in my hand. Between us we have 7 pencils.

You'd have no trouble working out, 'Okay, I must have 4 pencils'.

Well, if we wanted to get all mathematical about this (and hey, this is a maths book, so knock yourself out Adam), we could write:

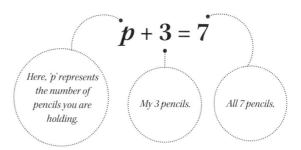

$$p + 3 = 7$$

Here, 'p' represents the number of pencils you are holding.

My 3 pencils.

All 7 pencils.

We call this letter 'p' a 'variable' or a 'pronumeral'.

You can probably look at this and just 'see' that the answer is 4. But algebra questions won't always be this easy. Let's do it mathematically. There are two simple rules to follow here:

1. We want to get the pronumeral by itself on one side of the equation with a number on the other side.
2. Currently the left- and right-hand sides of the equation are equal. To maintain this equality, whatever we do to one side of the equation we must do EXACTLY THE SAME THING to the other side.

So, here we go. Time for some algebra:

$$p + 3 = 7$$

Is the pronumeral by itself on one side of the equation? No – there is a 3 there as well. Can you see that the way to get from $p + 3$ to just p is to **subtract 3**? And remember: we have to do the same to each side of the equation.

$$p + 3 - 3 = 7 - 3$$

$p = 4$. The number of pencils you are holding is 4.

Now when algebra gets a bit harder, we are still just obeying those same two rules. Isolate the pronumeral by doing exactly the same to each side of the equation.

Tai buys 4 packets of his favourite biscuits. When he gets home he eats all 24 biscuits!!! Assuming each packet contains the same number of biscuits (and assuming Tai is probably feeling quite ill right now!), how many biscuits are in a packet?

Again, you can probably just see the answer, but ask yourself 'How am I seeing that?' This is probably how:

The question can be turned into this equation:

$$4 \times b = 24$$

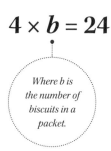

Where b is the number of biscuits in a packet.

Asking 'what number multiplies with 4 to give 24?' is the same as asking 'what is 24 ÷ 4?'

So, we would write:

$4 \times b = 24$ (divide each side of the equation by 4)
$b = 24 \div 4$
$b = 6$

There are 6 biscuits in each packet (and one very full Tai right now).

Indi gets a basic amount of pocket money each week, plus a bonus if she does extra chores. A fortnight ago she got a $3 bonus, last week she got a $4 bonus, but this week she got no bonus; in fact, mum took $1 off her for being a little bit naughty! She now has $21. What is her basic weekly pocket money?

Let's call her pocket money p. We could use 'm' for 'money' or 'd' for 'dollars' or 'x' because we like the letter x. It makes no difference to our answer.

Algebra goes back ages. The word comes from the book al-Kitāb al-Mukhtaṣ ar fi Ḥisāb al-Jabr wal-Muqābalah, which translates in English as The Compendious Book on Calculation by Completion and Balancing *(thanks Google!), written by the Big Brain of Baghdad, Al-Khwarizmi, in or around the year 825.*

The information in the question gives us this equation:

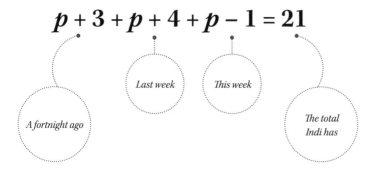

$$p + 3 + p + 4 + p - 1 = 21$$

Remember that the order in which you add and subtract numbers doesn't affect the result, so we can rearrange the left-hand side of the equation as:

$p + p + p + 3 + 4 - 1 = 21$ giving us
$3p + 6 = 21$ subtract 6 from each side
$3p = 21 - 6$
$3p = 15$ divide each side by 3
$p = 15 \div 3$
$p = 5$

Indi gets $5 a week pocket money.

After a bit of practice you won't need to take all these steps in such detail, but I can't recommend strongly enough that students go through every step in (almost painful!) detail early on, so that no mistakes creep in.

Like I said, you'll see a lot more of this in high school, but the rules remain the same. Good luck!

But it's on the internet!

Algebra can even help save you from being fooled by some internet memes! Last Christmas someone posted this on Instagram:

Mind blown. Have this as a crazy Xmas gift! Take your shoe size. Times by 5. Add 50. Times by 20. Add 1020. Subtract year you were born. Answer = your shoe size and your age.

And it works. My birthdate is in January 1969 (I know – I don't look it!!!) and my shoe size is 9.

So I get 9 → 45 → 95 → 1900 → 2920 → 951

My shoe size is 9 … and I was 51 at the time!!!

Now just pause for a second, take a deep breath and ask yourself, 'Have the laws of the cosmos really been replaced by witchcraft? Or is there another explanation for this?'

There is – and algebra can show it to us.

Call your age Λ and your shoe size S.

Now, it was late December 2020 when this was posted. So unless you were born in the last few days of the year,

2020 minus the year you were born will give you your age (e.g. if you were born in June 1980, you turned 40 in 2020 and 2020 − 1980 = 40).

Take your shoe size: S
Times by 5: 5 × S
Add 50: 5 × S + 50
Times by 20: 20 × (5 × S + 50) = 100S + 1000
Add 1020: 100S + 2020
Subtract the year you were born: 100S + (2020 minus the year you were born) = 100S + A

But A is almost certainly a one- or two-digit number. So 100S + A just appears as an S in front of your age. For example, shoe size 7, age 35, answer 735. Shoe size 12, age 8, answer 1208 and so on.

Thanks algebra! From now on I can ignore all those internet memes and concentrate on what matters #WhatTheDogDoin?

CURLY
QUESTIONS

IS 0 AN ODD OR EVEN NUMBER?

An even number, like 2, 4, 6 or 43,675,808, is a whole number that is divisible exactly by 2. This means when you divide the number by two you get a whole number as the answer.

If a whole number is not divisible by 2, for example 1, 3, 5 or 87,546,309, it is called an odd number.

And there's every chance your child will ask you at some stage, 'is 0 even or odd?'

Have a think about that yourself before you read on. Don't discount the fact that there are numbers that are neither even nor odd – for example $\frac{3}{4}$ or – 0.237. Maybe 0 is neither even nor odd?

Okay. Thinking time done, or 'whatever Adam, just tell me the answer please!' Either way let's go.

The number 0 is ... drum roll please ... EVEN.

Here are 3 ways to convince your child (and perhaps yourself!) that 0 is even.

1. If we divide the whole number 0 by 2, we get the whole number 0 as the answer. This satisfies the definition we started with.

2. If we add two even numbers the answer has to be even. You can see this in the examples 4 + 8 = 12, 16 + 16 = 32, and so on. Similarly, adding an even and odd number together has to give you an odd answer: 3 + 8 = 11 being an example. Well, any even number plus 0 remains even and any odd number plus 0 remains odd. Again, this shows 0 is even.

3. We don't talk about odd and even negative numbers all that much (well I do, but I know you don't), but when you understand that the counting numbers have to alternate even, odd, even, odd, even, odd ... it makes sense that 0 is even when you see it in the sequence ...

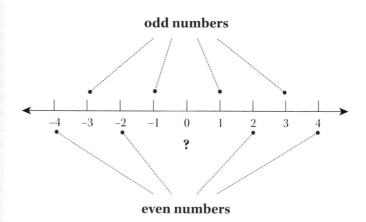

So there you go: 0 is an even number.

Question

WHAT IS INFINITY?

Kids love infinity. The moment it is introduced as a concept, either by a teacher or an older brother or sister, it takes hold like a forest fire and, before you know it, 'well my dad is as strong as infinity' is met with 'well my dad is as strong as infinity plus 10', and off we go.

Eventually your child will ask you, 'How big is infinity?'

Here is a beginner's guide to the wonderful thing that is infinity.

The most important thing to understand is that infinity, written ∞*, IS NOT A NUMBER. Think of infinity as a 'measure', meaning 'so big that it cannot be described by any whole number'. Maybe you would like to say 'uncountably large'.

An example is the counting numbers themselves. If you were to write out the list of all the positive whole numbers – 1, 2, 3... – how many numbers would be on your list?

5000? Clearly not, because once you got to 5000 you could write 5001, 5002 and just keep on going. Are there 1,000,000 numbers on your list? Again, I could count further. Have a look ahead to where we discuss a 'googol' to get your head around how massive numbers can quickly get, in just a few words of description. But even at these immensities, I could just keep on counting.

Most mind-bogglingly massive numbers that you could imagine are indescribably small compared to other numbers, that are in turn completely dwarfed by other numbers. And this process goes on ... forever.

The counting numbers never end. They can't be measured in terms of numbers. They are infinite.

Once you think of infinity as a measurement, you see that saying 'infinity plus 10' makes no sense. If you think there are 'lots' of people at the football and another busload of fans pulls up, you don't say there are 'lots plus 30' fans here; you still have 'lots'.

* In mathematics, a **lemniscate** curve is any of several figure-eight or ∞-shaped curves. The Latin lēmniscātus means 'ribboned', and it comes from the ancient Greek word λημνίσκος meaning 'ribbons'. So I guess that implies that infinity dances around forever like a ribbon tied back onto its own end, blowing gently in the breeze. (I'm making that last bit up, but it works for me.)

Extension!

Infinity wars

Here are a couple of mind games you can play with your kids to help them understand infinity. Now, when I say 'mind games' I don't mean those parental tricks and bluffs that get kids to accidentally do the washing up for you, I mean thought exercises that, while initially confusing, help you understand this most beautiful concept.

Mind game 1

You have a table with cards on it. Your cards are numbered 1, 2, 3, 4, 5, 6, 7, 8, 9, 10. Your child has the cards 2, 4, 6, 8 and 10 on a table in front of them.

Who has the most cards on their table?

It's not a trick question. Clearly, you have twice as many.

Now you have cards 1, 2, 3 ... 98, 99, 100 and your child has 2, 4, 6 ... 96, 98, 100. Do you agree you still have twice as many cards as your child?

Now you have cards 1, 2, 3 ... 999998, 999999 and 1,000,000 (did I mention, it's a MASSIVE table?). Your child has 2, 4, 6, 8 ...999998 and 1,000,000. You still have twice as many cards as your child.

Now you have cards for all the counting numbers on your table. The cards go on forever. Your child has all of the even counting numbers. Who has the most cards now? Clearly, you have some cards that your child doesn't – namely 1, 3, 5, 7 ... the odd ones. But who has the most cards? Think about this for a while.

Turns out, you both have the same infinite amount of cards. The easiest way to see that is to play this game.

You pick up a random card, say 7. Your child looks through their pile and finds card 14, and staples it to your card.

You grab another random card, say 12. Your child finds card 24 and again staples them together.

Every time you produce a card, your child produces the card bearing double that number and matches them up.

Can you see that every card in your pile can be uniquely matched, one-to-one, with every card on your child's table? Every one of your cards has a match and every one of their cards pairs with one and only one of yours.

We could list your cards like this:

Counting numbers		Even counting numbers
1	←——————→	2
2	←——————→	4
3	←——————→	6
4	←——————→	8
5	←——————→	10
6	←——————→	12
.		.
.		.
.		.

Your child's list of even numbers has been ordered so that they correspond one-to-one perfectly with the counting numbers. Every counting number has one and only one partner in the even numbers – and every even number is paired with one and only one counting number.

The set of even numbers is the same size as the set of counting numbers. We call these infinitely large sets 'countably infinite'.

Mind game 2 (we're going deeper)

Now your table has all of the counting numbers from 1 to infinity. But this time your child has all of the positive fractions on their table; like $\frac{3}{5}, \frac{1}{4}, \frac{27}{11}$ and so on. Note your child will have the counting numbers on their cards, written as $\frac{1}{1}, \frac{2}{1}, \frac{3}{1}$, etc.

Now, who has the most cards on their table?

Surely your child has? I mean, they have all of your whole numbers written as fractions with denominator 1, and all these other fractions!

That's what most people thought until the brilliant German mathematician George Cantor worked out a way to list the fractions again in one-to-one correspondence with the counting numbers.

Here is an insight into Cantor's most brilliant observation:

The secret is to look at a fraction in terms of its numerator plus its denominator. So, $\frac{3}{4}$ will be in the 'seven section' of the list. That section will also include $\frac{2}{5}$ and $\frac{6}{1}$ but not $\frac{1}{5}$ which will be in the 'six section'.

Every fraction goes into just one section of the list. Once we have all the fractions in a section, we can list them in terms of their numerators. Huh?

Take the 'five section'. The fractions, in order, are $\frac{1}{4}, \frac{2}{3}$,

$\frac{3}{2}$ *and* $\frac{4}{1}$. *The six section would be* $\frac{1}{5}$, $\frac{2}{4}$, $\frac{3}{3}$, $\frac{4}{2}$ *and* $\frac{5}{1}$.
   And so on.

Now we can list all of the positive fractions in one-to-one correspondence with the counting numbers. Check it out:

1 ←——→ $\frac{1}{1}$		11 ←——→ $\frac{1}{5}$
2 ←——→ $\frac{1}{2}$		12 ←——→ $\frac{2}{4}$
3 ←——→ $\frac{2}{1}$		13 ←——→ $\frac{3}{3}$
4 ←——→ $\frac{1}{3}$		14 ←——→ $\frac{4}{2}$
5 ←——→ $\frac{2}{2}$		15 ←——→ $\frac{5}{1}$
6 ←——→ $\frac{3}{1}$		16 ←——→ $\frac{1}{6}$
7 ←——→ $\frac{1}{4}$		17 ←——→ $\frac{2}{5}$
8 ←——→ $\frac{2}{3}$		18 ←——→ $\frac{3}{4}$
9 ←——→ $\frac{3}{2}$		19 ←——→ $\frac{4}{3}$
10 ←——→ $\frac{4}{1}$		20 ←——→ $\frac{5}{2}$

Perhaps you can see the list cascading down this grid here? Note that the grid is actually infinitely wide – this is just a snapshot of it!

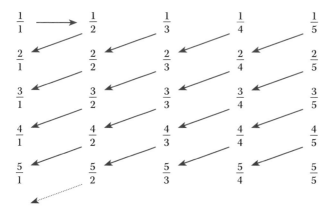

So every positive fraction is in a precise place on your child's list. This means they are arranged in one-to-one correspondence with the counting numbers. The set of all positive fractions (we call them the positive **rational numbers**) is countably infinite.

Mind game 3

Okay. Now we get serious. This time you have all of the counting numbers on your cards, but your child has the infinity of all the positive decimal numbers. This features suspects like 3.1 and 0.0043. It obviously includes all of the whole numbers, written as 1.0, 2.0, 3.0, etc. But your child also has numbers like π that go on forever as decimals, never ending or repeating.

Now who has the most cards on their table?

Again, Cantor comes to our rescue. It turns out that however your child lists their numbers, they can't be matched up one-to-one with the counting numbers.

The nub of the argument is this: list the infinity of the decimals.

$$0.04283...$$
$$1.53662...$$
$$4.03996...$$
$$2.0$$
$$8.88615...$$

If this is the list your child produces, you are going to create a number. Copy the first number on the list up until the decimal place, then add 1 to the first decimal place and make that the first entry after the decimal place in your new number.

Below, I've changed the 0 to a 1 in the first number on the list.

Moving to the second number on the list, we alter its second decimal place by 1 – here 3 became 4. Next line, next decimal place, and so on.

If a decimal has already terminated, just add a 1 in that place.

$$0.\overset{1}{\cancel{0}}4283...$$
$$1.5\overset{4}{\cancel{3}}662...$$
$$4.03\overset{0}{\cancel{9}}96...$$
$$2.0 \quad \overset{1}{\cancel{}}$$
$$8.8861\overset{6}{\cancel{5}}...$$

$$\downarrow \ \downarrow \downarrow \downarrow \downarrow \downarrow$$

$$0.14016...$$

Can you see that the new number you are creating, in this case 0.14016 ... is different to the first number on the list (its first decimal place is different)? Similarly, it's different in its second decimal place to the second number on the list. Similarly, our new number is different to the third, fourth, fifth and, in fact every number on your child's list.

Cantor showed that no matter how you try to list the decimals, you can create a new number not on the list.

The set of positive decimal numbers (we call them the positive **real numbers**) is a larger infinity than that of the counting numbers. We say this set is **uncountably infinite**.

So there's something you might not have known. Some infinites are bigger than others.

If you need a bit of a lie down after that, it's completely understandable. But wow, IMHO it's infinitely awesome!

Question

WHAT IS $\frac{1}{0}$?

What is $\frac{1}{0}$ and what about its big ugly cousin $\frac{0}{0}$?

$\frac{1}{0}$ is undefined. That means that mathematicians have literally not come up with an answer.

So $\frac{1}{0}, \frac{2}{0}, \frac{7}{0}$ are all undefined.

That can be a bit confusing, or unsatisfactory for people, because 1 and 0 are both numbers and fractions are certainly a 'thing', but let's look at why we can't define $\frac{1}{0}$ as being equal to any amount.

We all agree that $\frac{1}{1}$ = 1 and back in division by fractions we saw that $\frac{1}{\frac{1}{2}}$ = 2. Remember, we say this as 'how many halves are in one whole'.

This should be clear because it's asking 'if we break 1 into halves, how many halves do we get? We get 2'.

Similarly then, $\frac{1}{\frac{1}{3}}$ = 3 and $\frac{1}{\frac{1}{4}}$ = 4 and $\frac{1}{\frac{1}{10}}$ = 10 and $\frac{1}{\frac{1}{1000}}$ = 1000 and $\frac{1}{\frac{1}{1,000,000}}$ = 1,000,000 and so on.

So, as the number on the denominator approaches 0, the value of 1 divided by that number races off larger and larger. The fancy-pants mathematical way of saying this is, 'as the value of *n* approaches 0 from the positive side, the value of $\frac{1}{n}$ approaches infinity' or 'the limit of $\frac{1}{n}$ as *n* approaches 0 is infinity'. Using mathematical notation, we would write:

$$\lim_{n \to 0^+} \frac{1}{n} = \infty$$

You don't need to understand this notation, but I'm showing it to you just in case you want to leave it lying around on your desk so passers-by will think you are a BOSS!

Now, this observation about the value of $\frac{1}{n}$ for very small values of n leads some people to say that $\frac{1}{0} = \infty$. IT DOES NOT. Here are two reasons why:

1. No mathematical value can 'equal infinity'. Read about infinity again to remind yourself that infinity is a measurement or description of size, it is not a number. If you're thinking, 'But Adam, just up there you wrote " = " next to the limit statement' ... yes I did, but saying that a limit 'equals infinity' is a subtly different concept that you don't really need to fully understand to get what we need here. Apologies for any confusion!

2. Notice that $\frac{1}{n}$ as $n{\to}0$ **from the positive side.**

From the examples of:

$$\tfrac{1}{\frac{-1}{2}} = 1 \div \tfrac{-1}{2} = 1 \times \tfrac{-2}{1} = -2; \ \tfrac{1}{\frac{-1}{3}} = -3, \tfrac{1}{\frac{-1}{10}} = -10$$

and so on, you should be able to see that if the numbers approach 0 from the negative side, the value of 1 divided by those numbers races off to negative infinity, or

$$\lim_{n \to 0^-} \frac{1}{n} = -\infty$$

Look at you understanding mathematical notation you champion!

So I hope you agree that we can't say $\frac{1}{0} = \infty$ and $-\infty$ at the same time. This is why it has no defined value.

Another way to consider the value of $\frac{1}{0}$ is this:

When we say $\frac{12}{4} = 3$, we are effectively asking 'how many 4s do I have to add together to get 12?'

You should be able to see that because:
4 + 4 + 4 = 12 we also know that
$3 \times 4 = 12$, and hence
$\frac{12}{4} = 3$

Let's try this with $\frac{1}{0}$

To work it out we are asking, 'How many zeroes do I have to add together to get 1?'
    Well, 0 + 0 + 0 + 0 + 0 + ... can keep going as long as it wants. It will NEVER add up to 1.
    So there is no sufficient number of zeroes we can add together to get 1.

So again, $\frac{1}{0}$ makes no sense, so is 'undefined'.

Now for the even more curious case of $\frac{0}{0}$

I can think of three different arguments for the value of $\frac{0}{0}$. I'll spell them out and perhaps you can decide which one you like the most.

1. Let's divide the number n by itself and see what happens as n goes towards zero.

For $n = 1, \frac{n}{n} = \frac{1}{1} = 1$
For $n = 0.1, \frac{n}{n} = \frac{0.1}{0.1} = 1$
For $n = 0.01, \frac{n}{n} = \frac{0.01}{0.01} = 1$
For $n = 0.0000001, \frac{n}{n} = \frac{0.0000001}{0.0000001} = 1$

Similarly, if our values of n were very small negative numbers, the fraction $\frac{n}{n}$ would still equal 1 every time.

So clearly, as $n \to 0$, $\frac{n}{n} = 1$. So, $\frac{0}{0} = 1$.

2. Let's divide the number 0 by n and see what happens as n approaches 0.

For $n = 1$, $\frac{0}{n} = \frac{0}{1} = 0$
For $n = 0.1$, $\frac{0}{n} = \frac{0}{0.1} = 0$
For $n = 0.01$, $\frac{0}{n} = \frac{0}{0.01} = 0$
For $n = 0.0000001$, $\frac{0}{n} = \frac{0}{0.0000001} = 0$

Similarly, if our values of n were very small negative numbers, the fraction $\frac{0}{n}$ would still equal 0 every time.

So clearly, as $n \to 0$, $\frac{0}{n} = 1$. So, $\frac{0}{0} = 0$.

3. Let $\frac{0}{0} = z$ for some number z.
Then multiplying each side of this equation by 0, we would get $0 = 0 \times z$. But it doesn't matter what value we give z, the value of $0 \times z$ is always 0. So the equation $\frac{0}{0} = z$ holds for all possible values of z.

So $\frac{0}{0}$ = all possible numbers.

Which of these three arguments are you backing – does $\frac{0}{0}$ equal 1, 0 or all possible numbers?
    The problem is, they are all equally valid. So we can't choose one over the others.

We have to accept that $\frac{0}{0}$, like $\frac{1}{0}$, is also undefined.

Which, I guess, is either a bit of a bummer, or incredibly beautiful, depending on which way you look at it.

WHAT'S A 'GOOGOL'
AND A 'GOOGOLPLEX'?

A 'googol' is a famous large number in mathematics. A 'googolplex' is its much bigger sister.

First up, it's googol and googolplex. That's not a misprint. The search engine 'Google' is a misspelling. The guys who founded Google were originally going to call it 'Backrub' – imagine saying, 'What's the capital of Ethiopia ... I'll just quickly Backrub that!!!'* They decided they liked the concept of googol because there would be such a large amount of information on the internet. But they misspelled it, and on 15 September 1997 registered the website google.com

*The capital of Ethopia is Addis Adaba. I think it's awesome to teach kids capital cities and world geography!

Anyway, what is a googol?

In 1920 the American mathematician Edward Kasner was walking with his nine-year-old nephew, Milton Sirotta, and asked him for a name to give the number 1 followed by 100 zeroes. Milton suggested 'a googol'.

This is a massive number. The number 1 followed by 85 zeroes is a pretty good guess as to the number of fundamental particles in the entire universe! So a googol is the number of subatomic bits that make up everything in about 1,000,000,000,000,000 (yes that's one million billion, or a quadrillion!) versions of our visible universe!

Once you've got your head around that, take a deep breath, grab a glass of cold water and let's push on.

10,000,000,000, 000,000,000,000, 000,000,000,000, 000,000,000,000, 000,000,000,000, 000,000,000,000, 000,000,000,000, 000,000,000,000, 000,000,000,000, 000,000 'A googol, just hanging out.'

A googolplex is a mind-crushingly large number: 1 followed by a **googol zeroes**! Think about that. To try and get some perspective, 100 is 1 followed by two zeroes; a googol is 1 followed by 100 zeroes. Clearly a googol is gigantically bigger than 100. Now, 1000 is one followed by three zeroes. Compare that to 1 followed by 1000 zeroes – it's almost indescribably larger. Well, imagine how big a googolplex must be – 1 followed by a GOOGOL ZEROES!

So, is any number bigger than a googolplex?

I think it's great that kids encounter concepts like this that really stretch their minds. But you have to be careful once your child has heard of 'googolplex' – they might start saying, 'It's the biggest number that there is!' No, it's not. Is anything bigger than a googolplex?

Yes – 'a googolplex plus 7', for example. In fact, if you think about it, the counting numbers are infinite – they go on forever. Even though googolplex is fantastically larger than any number you'll need for any practical purposes, in the infinity of counting numbers it is vanishingly small.

If you remember powers you will know that $2^3 = 2 \times 2 \times 2 = 8$ and the **exponent** of 3 tells us to multiply three 2s together.

Well that means that googolplex^{googolplex} represents the absurdly large number we get when we multiply googolplex by itself googolplex times.

But I could then multiply that number by itself googolplex times, to get:

$$\text{googolplex}^{\text{googolplex}^{\text{googolplex}}}$$

and if I had nothing better to do (trust me – there have been many times when that was the case) I could multiply this ridiculously large number by itself over and over a grotesque number many times, giving us:

$$\text{googolplex}^{\text{googolplex}^{\text{googolplex}^{\text{googolplex}^{\text{googolplex}^{\text{googolplex}}}}}}$$

This is a tower of 6 googolplexes. What about a tower of googolplex googolplexes? Yes, it's a number. And because the counting numbers are infinite, even though this is beyond any practical size that you would ever need to describe anything, it is still vanishingly small in the infinity of counting numbers.

So yeah, maybe we will just leave it there for now!

Question

WHY ISN'T 1 A
PRIME NUMBER?

Ping! An SMS popped up on my screen. I could sense the urgency.

> 'Mate, Teddy (7), just asked me, "Dad, why isn't 1 a prime number?"
>
> I'm in the bathroom and I've stalled him for as long as I can. Please help!'

It was that SMS that gave me the idea for this entire book, so I guess we should answer my mate Ollie's question here.

Remember prime numbers? Six is NOT prime, because we can write $6 = 2 \times 3$. Seven is prime because we can write $7 = 1 \times 7$, but we can't write 7 as two smaller numbers multiplied together. We maths nerds say 'we can't write 7 as the product of two factors, other than the obvious example of 1×7'.

Just in case you're wondering, we call 6 a 'composite number'.

So the definition of a prime number is this:

A number n, greater than or equal to 2, is prime if it cannot be written as the product of any whole numbers apart from 1 and itself.

All well and good, but curious minds, like my mate's son Teddy, often wonder, 'Why isn't 1 a prime number? Why does the definition start at 2?'

I mean, $1 = 1 \times 1$ and there are no other positive whole numbers that multiply together to give us 1. One looks like a walk-up start, instant hall of famer, when it comes to prime numbers.

Well, here are two reasons why 1 isn't a prime number.

Reason 1:

I think we agree that when we multiply two prime numbers together, the answer has to be composite, yeah? Like in the example $2 \times 3 = 6$ from earlier.

Well, let's say 1 is prime, and I'm pretty sure we agree that 3 is prime. Let's multiply these two prime numbers together:

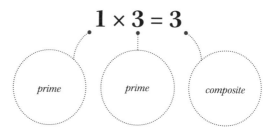

So we see that if we allow 1 to be prime, then 3 becomes both prime and composite at the same time.

I don't know about you, but I don't want to live in a universe like that!

Reason 2:

Another thing that happens if we allow 1 to be prime is that we lose a beautiful bedrock of arithmetic. Something so important we maths nerds call it 'the fundamental theorem of arithmetic'.

We can write 10 as the product of prime factors, namely $10 = 2 \times 5$ and you should be able to see that this is the only way 10 can be written as prime factors. We say that the prime factorisation of a number is unique.

Similarly, when I break 120 down into:

$$120 = 2 \times 2 \times 2 \times 3 \times 5$$

there is no other list of prime factors we could use.

But if 1 is prime, then $10 = 2 \times 5$ and $10 = 1 \times 2 \times 5$ and $10 = 1 \times 1 \times 2 \times 5$ and $10 = 1 \times 1 \times 1 \times 1 \times 1 \times 1 \times 2 \times 5$ and so on.

We go from having one unique factorisation into primes to having an infinite number of them. Ugh.

Don't be sad 1. We love you. You're like, super important. We've even got a special name for you ... a 'unit'.

You're just not prime.

Okay Ollie – you can come out of the bathroom now mate!

Extension!

Factor time

Write these numbers as the product of their prime factors:

36 $= 6 \times 6 = 2 \times 3 \times 2 \times 3 = 2^2 \times 3^2$

60 $= 6 \times 10 = 2 \times 3 \times 2 \times 5 = 2^2 \times 3 \times 5$

81 $= 9 \times 9 = 3 \times 3 \times 3 \times 3 = 3^4$

The X factor

Sometimes if a number is large or has lots of factors, it helps when finding prime factors to use what we call a 'factor tree'. Once you see one in operation, the name should make sense.

Factorise 120:

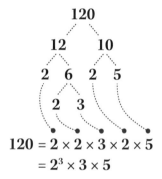

$$120 = 2 \times 2 \times 3 \times 2 \times 5$$
$$= 2^3 \times 3 \times 5$$

At each level, we factorise the numbers at the end of the branches. We keep going until we have all prime numbers and then rewrite the original number as their product.

Note that when we are factorising, it doesn't matter if we factorise in a different order. We will end up with the same answer as long as we don't make a mistake in our working. We could have started with 120 = 6 × 20 and proceeded as follows:

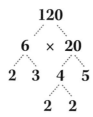

$$120 = 2 \times 3 \times 2 \times 2 \times 5$$
$$= 2^3 \times 3 \times 5$$

We would still end up with the same unique decomposition of 120 into prime factors.

Side note: If you are ever asked to find the factors of a number, say 120, you should know that a factor tree gives all the prime factors of a number, but may not give all factors. The best way to find the factors is to systematically go through all of the numbers less than the number and do lots of little divisions, then pair them.

We could write 120 as 2 × 60. We could also write it as 4 × 30; or 5 × 24; or 6 × 20.

You can check that 7 doesn't divide into 120. But 120 = 8 × 15 and 120 = 10 × 12. The next factor above 10 is 12 and we have already found it. So we are done.

The factors of 120 are:

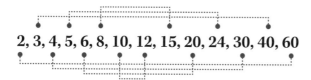

2, 3, 4, 5, 6, 8, 10, 12, 15, 20, 24, 30, 40, 60

Extension!

Prime time

Let's work up to a question that requires a few different skills from this book to solve.

If you remember our divisibility properties (see page 80) then it's pretty easy to check whether any number up to 100 is prime.

If they feature on the times tables they are not prime.

If they end in a 0, 2, 4, 6 or 8 then they are even, so they are not prime.

If they end in a 5 they are divisible by 5.

But there are some sneaky ones that can still get past this three-step defence plan.

Is 51 prime? You would be forgiven for answering 'yes' and not knowing that actually $51 = 3 \times 17$.

But if you had remembered the divisibility test for 3, you could add the digits of 51, and see that $5 + 1 = 6$, which is divisible by 3, hence 51 must have been divisible by 3. A quick short division (see page 74) gives you $51 = 3 \times 17$.

The only numbers that may slip through our hot little hands now are multiples of 7, for which there is no easy divisibility test.

So to check whether any number up to 100 (in fact, up to 120) is prime, once you've dismissed the obvious examples of even numbers and those ending in a 5, all you need to do is quickly sum the digits to test for divisibility by 3, and also divide by 7 either by hand or in your head. Try these:

Which of the following numbers are prime? If they are composite numbers, write them as their unique factorisation into primes.

$$37, 48, 49, 57, 71, 85, 91$$

37 clearly isn't divisible by 2 or 5. Let's test 3 as a factor; 3 + 7 = 10. Clearly 3 is not a factor of 10, so 3 is not a factor of 37. Is 7 a factor of 37? Well, 35 = 5 × 7 and 42 = 6 × 7, so 7 is not a factor of 37. Yes, 37 is prime.

48 = 6 × 8 = 2 × 3 × 2 × 2 × 2 = 2^4 × 3.

49 = 7^2. Students really should know this from their times tables.

57: 5 + 7 = 12 = 3 × 4, so 3 is a factor of 57; 57 = 3 × 19 and 19 is prime.

71: 7 + 1 = 8, so 3 is not a factor of 71; clearly 7 is a factor of 70 and the next multiple of 7 is 77, so 7 is not a factor of 71. So, 71 must be prime.

85 = 5 × 17.

91: 9 + 1 = 10, so 3 is not a factor of 91; the division algorithm shows us that 91 = 7 × 13.

Other cool prime number facts (okay I confess, I am a prime number junkie!)

The only even prime number is 2. After that all primes are odd.

The primes are infinite. There is no final largest prime number.

So, if we can start writing the list of prime numbers 2, 3, 5, 7, 11, 13 ... and the list is infinite, there must be, at any moment in time, a largest prime number that we know of. At the time I hit 'print' on this book, the largest prime number known to humanity was ... brace yourselves ...

$$2^{82,589,933} - 1$$

Yep, multiply 82,589,933 twos together, subtract one, and the absolute monster of a number that you end up with – all 24,862,048 digits of it (!!!) – is prime. If you printed out this single number as a copy of this book, you would need around 40 copies to write the entire number. Yet we know it is prime as confidently as we know 7 is prime. How awesome!

Big prime numbers underpin the major algorithms used in cybersecurity and internet banking. If someone discovered a way to factorise massive numbers really quickly, the implications for online security would be immense.

Anyway, that's a lot more information than I squeezed into my reply to my mate's text message. I hope you find prime numbers as awesome as I do!

WHERE DID NOTHING
COME FROM?

Though human beings have probably always understood the concept of nothing, or having nothing, the concept of zero is relatively new and only became fully operational in the fifth century AD. Before then, mathematicians all over the shop struggled to do the most basic of arithmetic calculations. Today, zero – both as a symbol (or numeral) and a concept meaning the absence of any quantity – allows us to do all sorts of amazing stuff like calculus and complicated equations. Zero even enabled the invention of computers. For something so abstract, it's incredibly important. For example, when you think about the numbers

100
or
2000
or
500,000

you most probably just see a digit followed by zeroes. In each of these numbers, the zero works like a 'placeholder' i.e. the three zeroes in 2000 tell us there are two thousands, not two hundreds, and so on. If you added or subtracted just a single zero, it would radically alter the amount.

The Babylonians were probably the first people to come up with a mark, two angled wedges, to signify that a number was absent from a column – just as the '0' in '1050' shows us that there are no hundreds in that number.

After the Babylonians, the Ancient Greeks (who stood on the shoulders of the Ancient Egyptians) actually made little progress on the whole zero debate, and it wasn't until 650 AD that an Indian mathematician named Brahmagupta from Bhinmal landed the killer blow.

Brahmagupta was a complete gun. Famous science historian George Sarton once called him 'the greatest of his time'. To represent zero, the Big-B used dots underneath numbers, which were referred to as śūnya, meaning 'empty', or kha, meaning 'place'. Brahmagupta understood how you could reach zero through addition and subtraction as well as the results of operations with zero. He didn't quite crack division by zero – that concept wouldn't be understood until Isaac Newton and Gottfried Leibniz got to work on it hundreds of years later.

We had to wait another 200 years or so before the circular representation of zero on a tablet in Gwalior. But hey, don't hold this against Brahmagupta, the man gave us something for nothing (geddit?) and was a bona fide genius!

The B-bomber himself – seen here sitting around doing, you guessed it, nothing!

Question

IS 0.99999999...
EQUAL TO 1 OR NOT?

This classic question has confused kids, muddled mums and dumbfounded dads down through the ages. To understand it, let's go back a step.

Remember decimals? They are numbers expressed using a series of digits after a decimal point. In the same way we express a number like 327 as 3 hundreds plus 2 tens plus 7 ones, 0.327 is equal to 3 tenths, 2 hundredths and 7 thousandths (check our Decimals chapter for more).

So $0.9 = \frac{9}{10}$ because the 9 immediately after the decimal place is in the 'tenths' column.

So when we look at 0.99 we see that the decimal goes past the tenths column and into the next decimal place, the 'hundredths' column.

$$\text{So, } 0.99 = \frac{9}{10} + \frac{9}{100} = \frac{90}{100} + \frac{9}{100} = \frac{99}{100}$$

Is that clear?

If so, you should be able to follow as we continue this pattern, and see that:

$$0.999 = \frac{999}{1000}, 0.9999 = \frac{9999}{10,000} \text{ and so on}$$

Any number 0.9...9 that is a string of 9s, is just equal to a fraction written as that string of 9s over 1 followed by as many 0s as there are 9s on the top. See that pattern?

$$\frac{9}{10}$$

$$\frac{99}{100}$$

$$\frac{999}{1000}$$

But what if the 9s go on ... FOREVER?

We write the number as 0.999... with the three dots implying it just keeps on going. Or we write:

$$0.\dot{9}$$

where the dot above the 9 suggests the 9 repeats forever.

This tends to blow kids' minds when they first see it ... and a fair few mums' and dads' minds as well when the memories come flooding back. And the typical question is 'my friend says this is the same as 1 but how can it be?'

Before I reveal the answer, ask yourself, 'What do I think? Is $0.\dot{9} = 1$ or not? And why do I think that?' An insight into why you think what you think may help you understand where your kid is at on this one.

And the answer is ... drum roll please ... yes;

$$0.\dot{9} = 1$$

Okay mind blown! Here's not one, not two, but four ways to see it (geez, Spence ... talk about value for money!). But seriously, I will show you four reasons here so you can appreciate that there are often many different ways to prove the same mathematical fact. Also, in my experience, for a brain buster like this, different people respond to different proofs. Hopefully there's at least one here that grabs you.

1. How close does $0.\dot{9}$ get to 1?

For our first proof, let's read along the list 0.9, 0.99, 0.999 and ask 'if we keep going (forever) how close to 1 would I have to get before I convinced you that $0.\dot{9} = 1$?'

It should be clear that the difference between 0.9 and 1 is the same as the difference between $\frac{9}{10}$ and 1, that is $\frac{1}{10}$. That's sort of close but still clearly they are $\frac{1}{10}$ apart.

What about 0.99? The distance from 0.99 (or $\frac{99}{100}$) to 1 is $\frac{1}{100}$. Closer, but still clearly they are not the same numbers. But as we add 9s after the decimal place, the difference between 0.9 ... 9 and 1 goes from $\frac{1}{1000}$ to $\frac{1}{10,000}$ to $\frac{1}{100,000}$ and so on and so on ... forever!

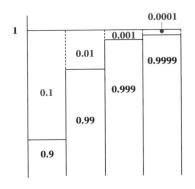

This diagram is not drawn to accurate scale (size). It just shows you how each term gets closer but always leaves a gap between itself and 1.

So, as we keep adding nines after the decimal point, the distance between 0.9...9 and 1 keeps getting smaller and smaller ... FOREVER.

So, 0.9̇ gets infinitely close to 1. That means, no matter how small a barrier you want to build between 0.9̇ and 1, the number 0.9̇ will get inside that barrier – on and on, forever.

For that reason 0.9̇ = 1.

2. If 0.9̇ = 1 then 1 - 0.9̇ should equal 0

This argument is a reworking of the first one.

Let's do some decimal subtraction:

$$
\begin{array}{r}
1.0 - \\
0.9 \\
\hline
0.1
\end{array}
\qquad
\begin{array}{r}
1.00 - \\
0.99 \\
\hline
0.01
\end{array}
\qquad
\begin{array}{r}
1.000 - \\
0.999 \\
\hline
0.001
\end{array}
$$

And so on.

Can you see that when we subtract a number that has a string of 9s after a decimal point from the number 1, the answer is 0.0...01 where the number of zeroes after the decimal point is one less than the number of 9s we started with?

So, $1 - 0.999\,999\,999\,999\,999 = 0.000000000000001$ (note the fifteen 9s and fourteen zeroes after the decimal place).

So can you see that when we calculate $1 - 0.\dot{9}$ if the string of 9s goes on forever, the string of 0s goes on forever after the decimal point and we never get to write the 1?

$$
\begin{array}{r}
1.00000... - \\
0.99999... \\
\hline
0.00000...
\end{array}
$$

If these zeroes _never_ end

and these 9s _never_ end

then these zeroes _never_ end.

So $1 - 0.\dot{9} = 0.\dot{0}$, which is 0 followed by a string of 0s; and is equal to 0.

If $1 - 0.\dot{9} = 0$ then $1 = 0.\dot{9}$.

These first two proofs are heavy stuff, so don't worry if it's a bit furry when you start. Trying to appreciate the infinity of 9s can really mess with your head.

Let's try a different tack.

3. Consider 0.$\dot{9}$ as a fraction!

We've already explored the relationship between decimals and fractions. In that chapter we saw a very important result about the fraction $\frac{1}{3}$.

So let's consider the fraction $\frac{1}{3}$. To write this as a decimal we do a short division of 3 into 1:

$$3 \overline{)\ 1.\overset{1\ 1\ 1\ 1}{0000}...} = 0.3333...$$

and see that we will just continue forever to repeat 'three into ten goes three remainder one. Carry the one. Three into ten goes three remainder one. Carry the one'.

$$\text{So } \tfrac{1}{3} = 0.\dot{3}$$

Well, by multiplying both sides of this equation by 3, it should be obvious that:

$$\tfrac{1}{3} \times 3 = 0.\dot{3} \times 3$$
$$1 = 0.333... \times 3$$
$$1 = 0.999...$$
$$1 = 0.\dot{9}$$

$$\text{So } 1 = 0.\dot{9}$$

Awesome stuff, isn't it!

4. A final, completely different way to look at this:

Let $x = 0.\dot{9}$
Then $10x = 9.\dot{9}$
(multiplying by 10 just moves the decimal point one place to the right).

So $10x - x = 9.\dot{9} - 0.\dot{9}$ ⋯⋯⋯⋯⋯•
$9x = 9$

$$9.9999... -$$
$$0.9999...$$
$$\overline{9.0000...}$$

So $9x = 9$ and therefore $x = 1$. But we started by saying $x = 0.\dot{9}$

So $0.\dot{9} = 1$.

Hopefully at least one of these proofs really gelled with you and you can now answer your curious child when they ask:

'Does 0.99999999... = 1 or not?'

My gifted child!

In many ways, having a child who is very good at mathematics can be just as challenging for mum or dad as having a child who is struggling. I'm often stopped in the street and asked, 'My child finds maths really hard, what can I do?' But just as often a parent looks at me with a glint of fear in their eyes and confesses, 'She's amazing at maths – I just can't keep up with her.'

So here are a few pointers on how to manage a child who really gets it and who really loves mathematics.

What should I do with my gifted child?

First up – let's get it out there. And in saying this I mean no offence whatsoever. YOUR CHILD IS NOT GIFTED*. There is nothing wrong with that. This advice applies just as much to 'curious', 'keen' and 'above average' children, so please press on and don't get too caught up in the terminology here!

If your child really loves maths and if they devour what they are given and are hungry for more, consider the following options.

Does your child's school run an extension program in mathematics?

Extension programs are great. Rather than just showing your third-grade child some stuff they will see soon after in year 4 (at which stage they will be bored in advance!), a good extension program will also cover material that sits outside the curriculum, but encourages problem solving

---

* *Of course there are such things as gifted children, but they are very rare. Depending on who you ask they comprise 2–10 per cent of school kids. 'Highly gifted' is significantly rarer still. Let alone 'genius', which is bandied about surprisingly often for a term that probably describes about 1 in 1000 kids.*

ability, logical thinking and other skills that will stand your child in good stead throughout their mathematical journey.

If there is not a program at your child's school, is there an after-school program nearby that your child could get permission to take part in?

More difficult problem solving?

APSMO (Australian Problem Solving Mathematical Olympiads) is an awesome Aussie institution that fosters excellence in problem solving and mathematical thinking. Curious kids and mathematical thinkers love puzzles and problems, which also help to develop the skills that will really flourish in high school. Can you encourage your child's school to enrol in the Maths Olympiad course? If not you can still purchase some of the amazing problem books on the APSMO website and open your child's eyes to a world of fun and challenging problems.

No Problemo

The Australian Maths Trust (AMT) runs competitions and programs that really extend talented students. I'm an ambassador for AMT's problem-solving site called 'Problemo'. It takes awesome questions from 40 years of the Australian Mathematics Competition and the Computational and Algorithmic Thinking Competition. It is sorted into age ranges and particular topics, with hints, answers and extensions of these problems into deeper work. See www.problemo.edu.au and go to the student portal. I'm biased because I'm an ambassador for the program, but honestly, a kid who loves maths could spend hours, weeks, months on Problemo and never get bored.

Other online resources

In the introduction I mentioned the NRICH program out of Cambridge University, which has a host of wonderful online resources for children of all ages. The Aussie site www.mathletics.com.au is also tremendous for kids who want to push themselves further.

Beyond mathematics

Get your child into things outside of mathematics too. For me, chess is a cracking game for young boys and girls (please more girls!!!) to play. And no matter how good you get at chess, there is always someone better waiting at the next tournament. You won't find a third-grade chess player thinking 'I've done all of this'.

One of my daughter's best-ever victories (she will be so embarrassed by me bringing this up) came as an 11-year-old against a 16-year-old boy, a good half metre taller than her.

Adam's daughter Ellie Spencer facing off against the brilliant Jennifer Zhang at the 2015 National u10 Girls Chess Championships. Ellie finished equal fourth and Jennifer became national champion. Photo supplied purely on the grounds that proud dads are allowed to embarrass their daughters!

In closing

The important thing here is, it doesn't matter whether your child is truly a 'once-in-a-generation' genius, a well above average student, or just loves mathematics and wants to do some more. If you take the initiative there are no end of ways you can feed the curious beast.

Again, hit me up at book@adamspencer. com.au to discuss ways of inspiring your maths-loving child whatever their level of ability.

ACKNOWLEDGEMENTS

None of this would be possible without the professionalism and smarts of Janine Sprakel. I was told you were 'the curriculum woman'. You are so much more – Respect².

Every project needs a test audience, especially when the subject comes so naturally to the author. A massive thanks to these wonderful parents and kids: Jo, Maya, Sam and Charlie Boyd; Sascha and Clodagh Carroll; Django Cooper; Saffron and Ziggy Francis; Dean and Jonty Fraser; Bailey and Rhys Hatgiantoniou; Cooper and Beau Hobbs; Lara and Cyrus Petrulis; Eva Tanner and Joshua and Annika Milotic; Samanta Vaglio and Surya Zanella. Your feedback was helpful, accurate and when needed gorgeously direct. You'll never meet most of the people you are helping with your generous support, but trust me, this book is the better for all of you.

To the 4 women in my life: **Mum** – you turned 80 this year and your endless belief in me, and support, has got me where I am today. Eternal thanks. **Olivia and Ellie** – watching you grow, learn and prepare to take on the world has been a blast. Thanks for dragging some of my pop culture references kicking and screaming into the 2020s. Dad couldn't love you more. **Leah** – from my first thinking of this project you've gone from someone I had never met, to friend, partner, fiancée and (by the time this book hits the shelves!) my wife. All that and the most supportive, caring and brutally thorough copyeditor I could ever hope to have met. I love you darling. #Us

And finally, to my publisher Pam Brewster for believing in this and steering, challenging and wrangling it into existence – thank you.

Published in 2021 by Hardie Grant Books, an imprint of Hardie Grant Publishing

Hardie Grant Books (Melbourne)
Wurundjeri Country
Building 1, 658 Church Street
Richmond, Victoria 3121

Hardie Grant Books (London)
5th & 6th Floors
52–54 Southwark Street
London SE1 1UN

hardiegrantbooks.com

Adam Spencer's Maths 101
ISBN 978 1 74379 761 7

 A catalogue record for this book is available from the National Library of Australia

10 9 8 7 6 5 4 3 2 1

Publisher: Pam Brewster
Education consultant: Janine Sprakel
Designer: Regina Abos
Typesetter: Eggplant Communications
Production Manager: Todd Rechner
Design Manager: Kristin Thomas

Colour reproduction by Splitting Image Colour Studio
Printed in China by Leo Paper Products LTD.